Teacher's Resource Masters

VOLUME 2

Topics 7–12

Home-School Connection Letters
Reteach to Build Understanding
Additional Vocabulary Support
Build Mathematical Literacy
Enrichment
Teaching Tools

enVisionmath®2.0
SCOTT FORESMAN · ADDISON WESLEY

ISBN-13: 978-0-328-...
ISBN-10: 0-328-...X

Pearson
Boston, Massachusetts

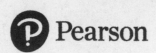

ISBN-13: 978-0-328-95084-3
ISBN-10: 0-328-95084-X

Accelerated Grade 7
Volume 2: Topics 7–12

Topic 11 Congruence and Similarity

Topic 12 Solve Problems Involving Surface Area and Volume

Name _____

Analyze and Solve Linear Equations

Dear Family,

   Your child is learning to interpret, represent, and solve multistep equations in mathematical and real-world contexts. Your child is also studying graphs and equations of lines in the coordinate plane and learning to identify slopes and y-intercepts. Here is an activity to help your child understand connections between linear equations and graphs.

Slope and Graphs

Materials: All cards numbered 2 through 6 from a standard deck of playing cards; graph paper

Step 1 Shuffle the cards and place two cards face up. Red cards represent negative numbers and black cards represent positive numbers.

Step 2 Working with your child, use the two numbers to create a slope ratio, $m = \frac{rise}{run}$.

For example, a red 2 and a black 6 can be used to create the ratios $\frac{-2}{6}$ or $\frac{6}{-2}$.

Step 3 Graph the equation $y = mx$. Starting at the origin, move vertically the number of units indicated by the rise—down if the rise is negative and up if the rise is positive. Then move horizontally the number of units indicated by the run—left if the run is negative and right if the run is positive. Graph a point and draw a line through this point and the origin.

Observe Your Child

Focus on Mathematical Practices
Model with mathematics

Help your child become proficient with this Mathematical Practice. Take a stroll or drive with your child and look for real-world examples of slope. For example, compare the slope of a wheelchair ramp with the slope of a roof. Discuss the importance of the slope in each design.

Nombre _____

Analizar y resolver ecuaciones lineales

Estimada familia:

Su hijo o hija está aprendiendo a interpretar, representar y resolver ecuaciones de varios pasos en contextos matemáticos y de la vida diaria. También está estudiando gráficas y ecuaciones lineales en el plano de coordenadas, y está aprendiendo a identificar pendientes e interceptos en y. Esta es una actividad que ayudará a su hijo o hija a comprender las relaciones entre las gráficas y las ecuaciones lineales.

Pendientes y gráficas

Materiales: Cartas numeradas del 2 al 6 de una baraja de cartas común, papel cuadriculado

Paso 1 Mezcle las cartas y coloque dos boca arriba. Las cartas rojas representan números negativos y las cartas negras representan números positivos.

Paso 2 Con su hijo o hija, usen los dos números para crear una razón para la pendiente

$$m = \frac{\text{distancia vertical}}{\text{distancia horizontal}}.$$

Por ejemplo, un 2 rojo y un 6 negro se pueden usar para crear las razones $\frac{-2}{6}$ o $\frac{6}{-2}$.

Paso 3 Grafiquen la ecuación $y = mx$. Comiencen en el origen y muévanse en sentido vertical tantas unidades como indique la distancia vertical (hacia abajo si la distancia vertical es negativa y hacia arriba si es positiva). Luego, muévanse en sentido horizontal tantas unidades como indique la distancia horizontal (hacia la izquierda si la distancia horizontal es negativa y hacia la derecha si es positiva). Marquen un punto y dibujen una recta que pase por este punto y por el origen.

Observe a su hijo o hija

Enfoque en las Prácticas matemáticas
Representar con modelos matemáticos.

Ayude a su hijo o hija a adquirir competencia en esta Práctica matemática. Den un paseo a pie o en carro y busquen ejemplos de pendientes de la vida diaria. Por ejemplo, comparen la pendiente de una rampa para sillas de ruedas con la pendiente de un techo. Comenten la importancia de la pendiente en cada diseño.

Johann sold 9 of his video games online. The next day, he sold 27 video games. He collected a total of $900. If Johann charged the same amount for each video game, how much did he sell each game for?

$$9x + 27x = 900$$ Write an equation.

$$36x = 900$$ Combine like terms.

$$\frac{36x}{36} = \frac{900}{36}$$ Divide each side by 36.

$$x = 25$$ Simplify.

Johann sold each game for $25.

Joshua makes earrings to sell at craft fairs. Each pair of earrings contains the same number of wooden beads as glass beads. For each pair, Joshua spends a total of $0.29 on the wooden beads and $0.11 on the glass beads. How many pairs of earrings, x, can Joshua make if he has $20 to spend on beads?

1. Use the information in the problem to complete the bar diagram.

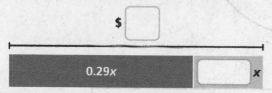

2. Write an equation to represent the bar diagram.

3. What are the like terms in your equation from Exercise 2? Rewrite the equation by combining the like terms.

4. Divide each side of the equation by the same number to solve for x. How many pairs of earrings can Joshua make?

On the Back!

5. Irene owns a bakery. For each cake, she spends $\frac{1}{4}$ of an hour to make frosting and $\frac{2}{5}$ hour to decorate. How many cakes can Irene frost and decorate in $3\frac{1}{4}$ hours?

 7

Name _____

Each section of the graphic organizer contains a vocabulary term and examples of the term. Use the list below to complete the graphic organizer.

coefficients	terms	variables
$4x$	$2y$	$-3y$
2 in $2y$	-3 in $-3y$	x in $4x$

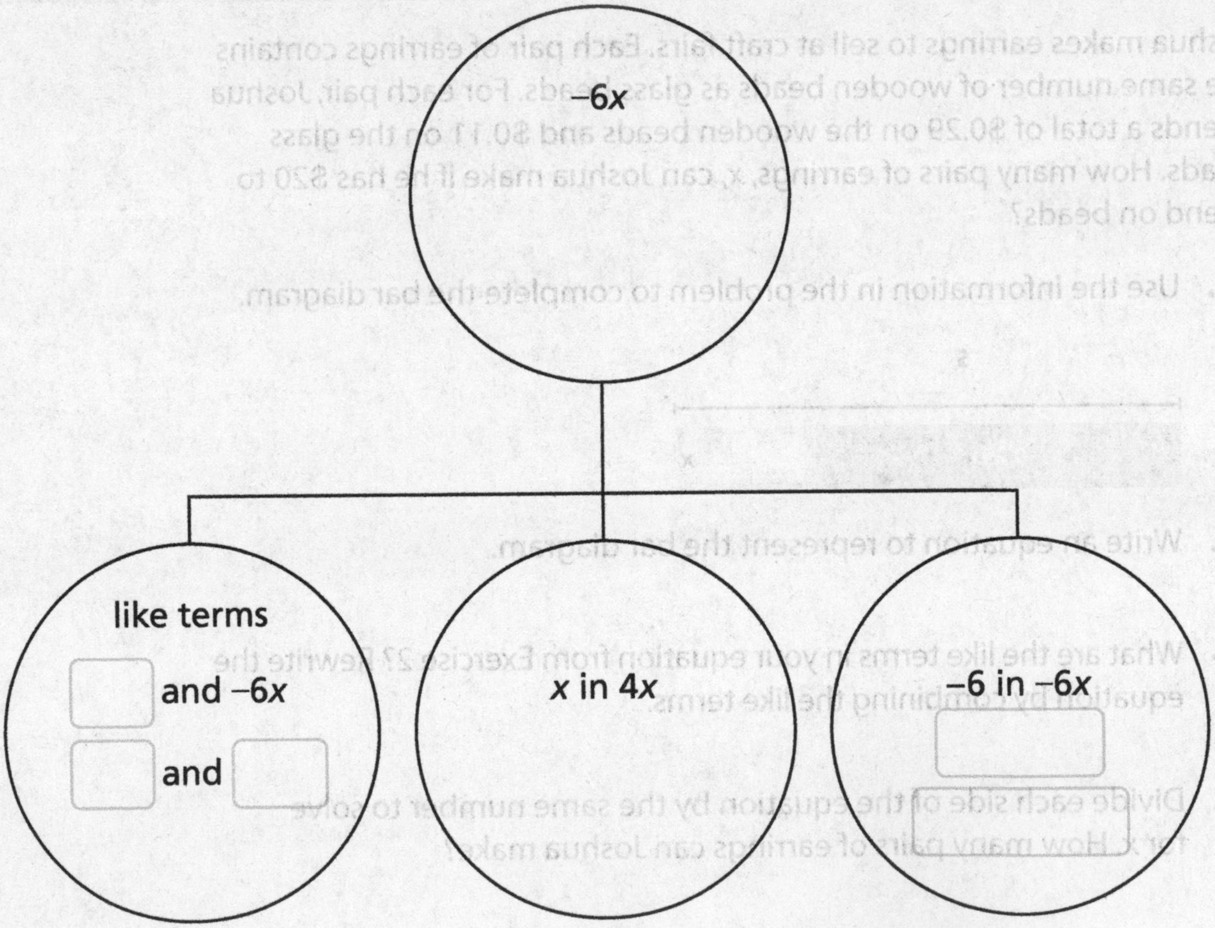

$-6x$

like terms

☐ and $-6x$

☐ and ☐

x in $4x$

-6 in $-6x$

☐

Name _____

**Read the problem below. Then answer the questions to
understand the problem.**

Taylor buys a skateboard for $51.84. The price includes 8% sales tax.
The equation $p + 0.08p = 51.84$ can be used to find the price of the
skateboard before sales tax. What is the price of the skateboard before
the sales tax is applied?

1. Underline the question that you need to answer.

2. What does the variable p represent?

3. Circle the expression below that represents the sales tax.

    p $0.08p$ $p + 0.08p$ 51.84

4. Explain the meaning of the expression $p + 0.08p$.

5. Highlight the like terms in the given equation.

6. Why is it necessary to combine like terms to solve the given
    equation?

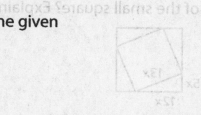

1. Two identical rectangles and squares *R* and *T* are arranged to form a larger square as shown. The area of square *R* is 1 square inch and the perimeter of each rectangle is 7 inches. What is the perimeter of square *T*? Explain.

```
┌──────────┬───┐
│          │ R │
│       ───┴───┤
│   T          │
│              │
└──────────────┘
```

2. Four identical right triangles whose sides measure 3*x*, 4*x*, and 5*x* are arranged to form a small square inside a large square, as shown. The perimeter of each right triangle is 60 cm. What is the perimeter of the small square? Explain.

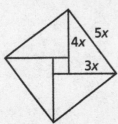

3. Four identical right triangles whose sides measure 5*x*, 12*x*, and 13*x* are arranged to form a small square inside a large square, as shown. The perimeter of the large square is 17 units. What is the perimeter of the small square? Explain.

Rachel has saved $200 and spends $25 each week. Roy just started saving
$15 per week. In how many weeks will Rachel and Roy have the same
amount of money saved?

$$200 - 25x = 15x$$ Write an equation.

$$200 - 25x + 25x = 15x + 25x$$ Add 25x to both sides.

$$200 = 40x$$ Combine like terms.

$$\frac{200}{40} = \frac{40x}{40}$$ Divide both sides by 40.

$$5 = x$$ Simplify.

Rachel and Roy will have the same amount of money saved in 5 weeks.

Aldon and Jamal raised the same amount of money for the school fundraiser. Aldon
donated $40 and sold 12 tickets for the school raffle. Jamal donated $25 and sold
15 tickets for the raffle. What was the cost of each raffle ticket?

1. Complete the bar diagram below.

2. What expression represents the total amount of money that
   Aldon raised?

3. What expression represents the total amount of money that
   Jamal raised?

4. Write an equation that shows that Aldon and Jamal raised the
   same amount of money.

5. Solve your equation for x. What was the cost of each raffle ticket?

On the Back!

6. Ray and Claudia are writing in journals. Ray has written 16 pages
   and he now writes 2 pages every day. Claudia has written only
   2 pages, but she now writes 4 pages every day. In how many days
   will they have written the same number of pages?

Use each of these words or phrases once to complete the sentences.

coefficient	constant	equation	like terms

1. A term that has no variable factor is a(n) _____.

2. In an expression, _____ have exactly the same variable factors.

3. A statement that two expressions are equal is a(n) _____.

4. When a term has a variable, the numerical factor is called the _____.

For 5–8, use the given equation to complete each sentence.

5. In the equation $0.5x - 8 = 1.5$, the decimal coefficient is _____.

6. In the equation $\frac{3}{4}y + \frac{1}{2} = 3\frac{1}{4}$, the fractional coefficient is _____.

7. In the equation $-2 - 6b = 32$, the negative coefficient is _____.

8. In the equation $5x + 9 = 3x$, _____ and _____ are like terms.

Name _____

**Read the problem. Then answer the questions to identify
the steps for solving the problem.**

Toni and Nicky each earn a weekly salary plus commission selling
eyeglass frames. Toni earns a weekly salary of $800 plus a 7%
commission on her weekly sales. Nicky earns a weekly salary of $600
plus a 9% commission on her weekly sales. What number of eyeglass
frames sold will result in Toni and Nicky earning the same amount for
the week?

1. Circle the words that describe Toni's weekly earnings. Underline
   the words that describe Nicky's weekly earnings.

2. What is the first step in writing an equation to solve the problem?

3. Can you use the same variable to represent the unknown amount
   of sales for both Toni and Nicky? Explain.

4. Circle the expressions that represent Toni's total earnings and
   Nicky's total earnings for a week in which their weekly sales is x.

   $600 + 9x$ and $800 + 7x$ $\qquad\qquad$ $600 + 0.09x$ and $800 + 0.07x$

   $600 \cdot 0.09 \cdot x$ and $800 \cdot 0.07 \cdot x$ $\qquad$ $600 - 0.9x$ and $800 - 0.7x$

5. How can you use the two expressions from Exercise 4 to solve the
   problem? Explain.

Name _____

The online auction website, Online Sales, pays its vendors half of the selling price of each item sold and deducts a listing fee of $5 per item. Another online auction site, Sales Alive, pays its vendors 40% of the selling price of the item with no listing fee.

1. Complete the table of values. How can a vendor use the table to determine which website to choose to sell a particular item? Explain.

Item's selling price ($)	Amount vendor receives from Online Sales ($)	Amount vendor receives from Sales Alive ($)
20		
30		
40		
50		
60		
70		

2. What equation represents the selling price for which a vendor receives the same amount of money from either website? How does the table show the solution to the equation?

3. Suppose Sales Alive begins charging a listing fee of $2.75 per item sold. Write an equation to find the selling price for which a vendor receives the same amount from either website and solve. Why might this problem be difficult to solve by making a table of values?

Name _____

Solve the equation $4(3x + 5) = 6(x + 8) - x$.

$4(3x + 5) = 6(x + 8) - x$	
$12x + 20 = 6x + 48 - x$	Use the Distributive Property.
$12x + 20 = 5x + 48$	Combine like terms.
$7x + 20 = 48$	Subtract $5x$ from both sides.
$7x = 28$	Subtract 20 from both sides.
$x = 4$	Divide both sides by 7.

Rajan bought 5 copies of a book to give as gifts. The book was on sale for $5 off the original price. The total that Rajan spent on 5 books was $2 more than he would have spent on 4 copies of the book at the original price. What was the original price?

1. Complete the bar diagram below.

| Sale Price | $x - 5$ | | | | |
| Original Price | x | | | | 2 |

2. Complete the equation that represents the bar diagram.

   $5(\boxed{} - \boxed{}) = \boxed{} + \boxed{}$

3. Fill in the steps to solve the equation.

$5x - \boxed{} = 4x + 2$	Use the $\boxed{}$ Property.
$5x - \boxed{} - 25 = 4x - 4x + 2$	Subtract $\boxed{}$ from both sides.
$\boxed{} - 25 = 2$	Combine like terms.
$x - 25 + \boxed{} = 2 + \boxed{}$	Add 25 to both sides.
$x = \boxed{}$	Simplify.

4. What was the original price of the book?

On the Back!

5. Joshua scored the same number of points in each of his last 3 basketball games. He scored 8 fewer points in each of those games than he scored in his best game. The total number of points that Joshua scored in the last 3 games is equal to twice the number of points he scored in his best game. How many points did Joshua score in his best game?

Name _____

Complete the vocabulary chart.

Word or Phrase	Definition	Example
coefficient		5 is the coefficient for $5a$. -2 is the coefficient for $-2w$.
Distributive Property	For every real number a, b, and c: $a(b + c) = ab + ac$ $a(b - c) = ab - ac$	
like terms		$\frac{1}{2}y$ and $6y$ $-0.3x$ and $1.4x$
multistep equation	A multistep equation is an equation that requires multiple steps to solve.	
variable		w, x, or y

Name _____

**Review the Key Concept from the lesson. Then answer the
questions to help you understand how to read a Key Concept.**

KEY CONCEPT

When solving multistep equations, sometimes you distribute first, and then
combine like terms.

$$7(5 + 2x) + x = 65$$

$$35 + 14x + x = 65$$

Sometimes you combine like terms first, and then distribute.

$$8(5x + 9x + 6) = 160$$

$$8(14x + 6) = 160$$

1. Highlight the parts of each equation that must be simplified before
   the equation can be solved.

2. What property do the arrows represent?

3. Why is it necessary to use the Distributive Property first and then
   combine like terms to solve $7(5 + 2x) + x = 65$?

4. What do the parentheses mean in the expression $8(5x + 9x + 6)$?

5. Why do you first combine like terms and then use the Distributive
   Property to solve $8(5x + 9x + 6) = 160$?

Use the clues to find the value of each variable.

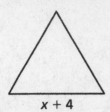

$x + 4$

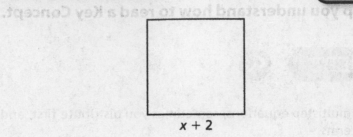

$x + 2$

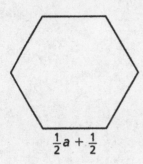

$\frac{1}{2}a + \frac{1}{2}$

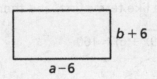

$b + 6$

$a - 6$

The triangle is an equilateral triangle.

The hexagon is a regular hexagon.

The perimeter of the triangle is equal to the perimeter of the square.

The perimeter of the hexagon is 12 times the value of x.

The area of the rectangle is the same as the area of the square.

$x = $ ☐

$a = $ ☐

$b = $ ☐

A one-variable equation can have infinitely many solutions, no solutions, or one solution.

Infinitely Many Solutions	**No Solution**	**One Solution**
$9(2x + 1) = 3(6x + 3)$	$2(2x + 5) = 4(x + 2)$	$3x - 8 = 2x + 4$
$18x + 9 = 18x + 9$	$4x + 10 = 4x + 8$	$x - 8 = 4$
$9 = 9$	$10 \neq 8$	$x = 12$
Solving the equation results in a true statement.	Solving the equation results in an untrue statement.	Solving the equation results in one value for the variable.

Carlo and Helen spend the same amount of money on art supplies. Carlo buys 4 glue sticks and spends $3 on glitter. Helen buys 2 glue sticks, and she spends $3.75 on tape and $2.75 on paint. What is the cost, x, of each glue stick?

1. Complete the bar diagram below.

Carlo		$3
Helen	2x	$	$2.75

2. Complete the steps to write and solve an equation for x.

$$\boxed{} + 3 = 2x + \boxed{} + \boxed{}$$

$$4x + 3 = 2x + \boxed{}$$

$$4x - \boxed{} + 3 = 2x - \boxed{} + 6.5$$

$$\boxed{} + 3 = 6.5$$

$$2x + 3 \boxed{} = 6.5 - \boxed{}$$

$$2x = \boxed{}$$

$$\frac{2x}{\boxed{}} = \frac{3.5}{\boxed{}}$$

$$x = \boxed{}$$

3. What is the cost of each glue stick?

On the Back!

4. How many solutions does the equation $3(4x + 1) = 6(2x - 5)$ have?

Use each of these words or phrases once to complete the sentences.

| Distributive Property | inverse operations | like terms |
| infinitely many solutions | no solution | |

1. To solve a one-variable equation, it may be necessary to first multiply by using the _____.

2. The next step is to combine _____ as needed.

3. Then solve for the variable by applying _____.

4. If solving leads to a true equation, then the equation has _____.

5. If solving leads to an untrue equation, then the equation has _____.

After completing the steps for solving an equation, the following equation results. Determine if each equation has *one solution*, *infinitely many solutions*, or *no solution*.

6. $7 = 7$ _____

7. $x = 0$ _____

8. $1 = -4$ _____

9. $-3 = x$ _____

10. $0 = 0$ _____

Read the problem. Then answer the questions to help you understand how to solve the problem.

Classify each equation as having one solution, no solution, or infinitely many solutions.

$$3x + 8 = 17 \qquad 2x + 8 = 2(x + 4) \qquad x + 4 = x - 4$$

1. Highlight what you need to determine for each equation.

2. What does it mean for an equation to have no solution?

3. How can you tell when a one-variable equation has no solution?

4. What does it mean for an equation to have infinitely many solutions?

5. How can you tell when a one-variable equation has infinitely many solutions?

6. Solving one of the equations results in $x = 3$. What can you conclude about the number of solutions for this equation?

You have seen that an equation may have one solution, no solutions, or infinitely many solutions.

1. An equation has the form $ax + b = ax + d$, where a, b, and d are real numbers. What can you conclude about the number of solutions to this equation? Explain.

2. For what value of k does the equation $5x - 32 = kx + 3$ have no solution?

3. For what value of k does the equation $6(x + 1) + 2 = 3\left(\frac{k}{5}x + 1\right) + 3$ have no solution?

4. For what value of k does the equation $12x + 17 = 4(3x + 2) + k$ have infinitely many solutions?

5. For what value of k does the equation $3(5 + x) + kx + 8 = 7(2x + 3) + (x + 2)$ have infinitely many solutions?

6. Is there a value of k for which the equation $2(kx + 2) + 9 = 4(x + k) + 1$ has infinitely many solutions? Explain.

LaShonda and Marilyn are saving for a vacation. Who is saving more money per week?

LaShonda's Savings

Weeks	5	6	7	8
Amount Saved (in $)	125	150	175	200

LaShonda's unit rate $= \dfrac{\text{amount saved}}{\text{weeks}} = \dfrac{\$125}{5 \text{ weeks}} = \dfrac{\$25}{1 \text{ week}}$

Marilyn's unit rate is represented by the point (1, 20). She is saving $20 per week. LaShonda is saving more money per week.

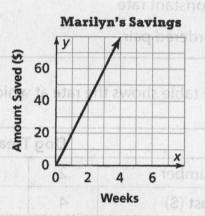

Marilyn's Savings

Two grocery stores charge different amounts for Henry's favorite olives. At which store will Henry pay a lower price per pound for olives?

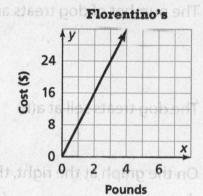

Florentino's

Mangio's

Pounds	3	4	5	6
Cost ($)	18	24	30	36

1. What is the unit cost of the olives at Mangio's?

2. What point on the graph represents the unit cost at Florentino's? What is the unit cost?

3. At which store will Henry pay a lower price per pound for olives? Explain.

On the Back!

4. Noah ran a total of 54 miles over 9 days. The graph relating Greta's total distance to the number of days passes through the points (0, 0) and (5, 45). Who ran more miles per day?

Use the list below to complete the sentences. Use each term once.

constant rate	greater than	less than
ordered pair	proportional relationship	unit rate

The table shows the rate at which Brianna sells homemade dog treats.

Dog Treats				
Number	2	5	8	12
Cost ($)	4	10	16	24

1. The number of dog treats and the cost are in a(n) _____
   _____ .

2. The dog treats sell at a(n) _____ of $4 for 2 treats.

3. On the graph at the right, the point (1, 2) represents
   the _____ of $2 for each dog treat.

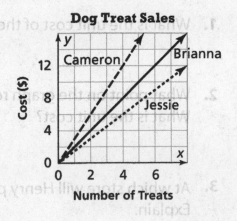

Dog Treat Sales

4. The _____ (5, 10) lies on the line that
   represents the rate at which Brianna sells dog treats.

5. The equation $y = 3x$ can be used to find the cost,
   y, for x dog treats sold by Cameron. Cameron sells

   dog treats at a rate that is _____
   Brianna's rate.

6. The point (4, 6) lies on the line that represents the rate at which
   Jessie sells dog treats. Jessie sells dog treats at a rate that is
   _____ Brianna's rate.

Name _____

**Read the problem. Then answer the questions to
understand the problem.**

The graph shows two proportional relationships.
How does the rate of Vehicle 1 compare with the rate
of Vehicle 2?

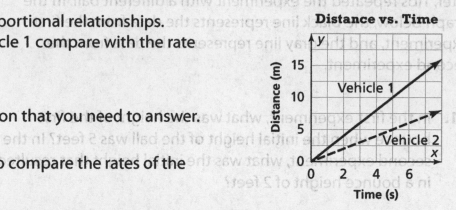

Distance vs. Time

1. Underline the question that you need to answer.

2. What does it mean to compare the rates of the
   two vehicles?

3. Which vehicle has the steeper graph?

4. After 5 seconds, how far has Vehicle 1 traveled? Use this
   information to write a unit rate for Vehicle 1.

5. After 5 seconds, how far has Vehicle 2 traveled? Use this
   information to write a unit rate for Vehicle 2.

6. Do you need the answers from Exercises 4 and 5 to solve this
   problem? Explain.

Name _____

For a science experiment, Tibs dropped a ball from various heights and recorded the height of the first bounce. A few days later, Tibs repeated the experiment with a different ball. In the graph below, the black line represents the data from the first experiment, and the gray line represents the data from the second experiment.

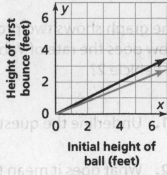

1. In the first experiment, what was the height of the first bounce when the initial height of the ball was 5 feet? In the second experiment, what was the initial height that resulted in a bounce height of 2 feet?

2. Which line is steeper? Explain what this means in terms of unit rates.

3. Tibs estimates that the line representing the first experiment passes through (1, 0.5). What is a reasonable estimate for the point whose x-coordinate is 1 on the line representing the second experiment? What is the meaning of these points in terms of unit rates? Explain.

4. Tibs performs a third experiment with another ball. For an initial height of 5 feet, the bounce height was between the bounce heights for the other experiments. Is it possible that for some initial height, the bounce height will be the same as either of the other experiments? Explain.

In order to finish reading a book by the assigned date, Caleb plans to read the same number of pages each day, as shown in the graph. What is the slope of the line?

The rise is 200 pages. The run is 4 days.

$$\frac{\text{rise}}{\text{run}} = \frac{200 \text{ pages}}{4 \text{ days}} = 50 \text{ pages per day}$$

The slope of the line is 50.

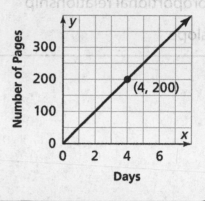

The graph relates the time in minutes and the number of laps Jerry must run around the track in order to meet his goal for the track meet. What is the slope of the line?

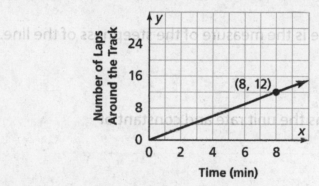

1. What is the rise between the points (0, 0) and (8, 12)?

2. What is the run between the points (0, 0) and (8, 12)?

3. What is the slope of the line?

On the Back!

4. Christina made a graph to describe the distance she walked on her backpacking trip. She plotted miles on the y-axis and the number of days on the x-axis. She graphed a point at (0, 0) and another point to show she walked 14 miles in 8 days and drew a line that passes through the points. What is the slope of the line?

Use each of these terms or phrases once to complete the sentences.

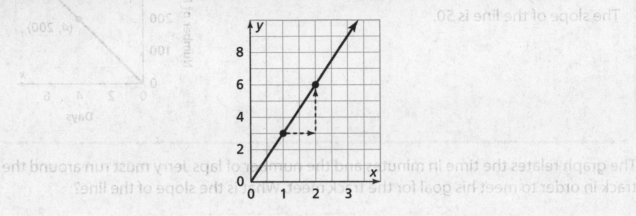

proportional relationship	rise	run
slope	$x_2 - x_1$	$y_2 - y_1$

1. The _____ of a line is the measure of the steepness of the line.

2. The slope is the same as the unit rate and constant of proportionality in a _____.

3. In the slope ratio, the change in the *x*-coordinates from one point to another on a line is the _____.

4. In the slope ratio, the change in the *y*-coordinates from one point to another on a line is the _____.

5. The slope between two points on a line can be found using the ratio $\dfrac{\text{change in } y\text{-coordinates}}{\text{change in } x\text{-coordinates}}$ or [_____] and [_____].

Name _____

Read the problem and connect it to the graph.

The graph represents the cost, *y*, of *x* pounds of granola at a market. What is the slope of the line? What does it mean in the problem situation?

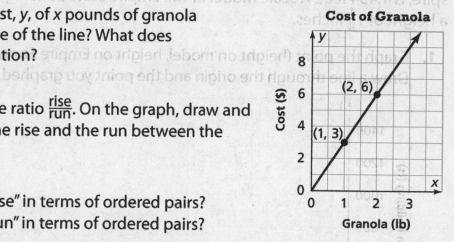

Cost of Granola

1. The slope of a line is the ratio $\frac{rise}{run}$. On the graph, draw and label arrows to show the rise and the run between the two labeled points.

2. How do you find the "rise" in terms of ordered pairs? How do you find the "run" in terms of ordered pairs?

3. Highlight the *y*-values you would use to find the slope of the line in one color and *x*-values in another color.

4. Does the order in which you subtract the coordinates matter? Explain.

5. What quantity does the *x*-axis represent? What quantity does the *y*-axis represent? How does this information help you determine the meaning of the slope in this problem?

The height of the Empire State Building, including its antenna spire, is 1,454 feet. A scale model of the Empire State Building has a height of $7\frac{1}{4}$ inches.

1. Graph the point (height on model, height on Empire State Building). Draw a line through the origin and the point you graphed.

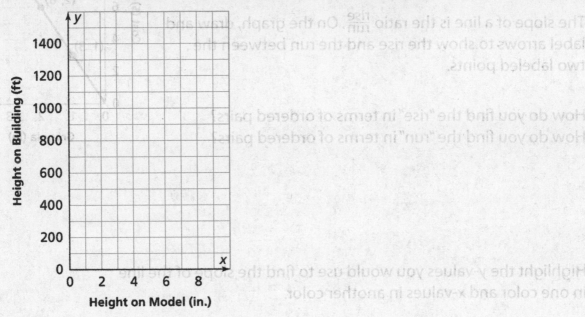

2. What is the slope of the line? What does it mean in the problem situation?

3. The antenna spire of the Empire State Building is 203 feet tall. About how tall should the antenna spire on the model of the Empire State Building be? Does the point (height of spire on model, height of spire on building) appear to lie on the line you graphed?

4. An observation deck on the Empire State Building is at a height of 1,050 feet. What is the height of the deck on the model?

5. The height of the White House, in Washington, DC, is 70 feet. A scale model of the White House has a height of 4.5 inches. Does the model of the White House have the same scale as the model of the Empire State Building? Explain.

The manager of a customer service center made
this graph to show the average number of customer
concerns, y, he would like his department to resolve
each hour, x. Write the equation of the line that
represents this relationship.

The slope is $\frac{rise}{run} = \frac{28}{8} = 3.5$.

The equation of the line is $y = 3.5x$.

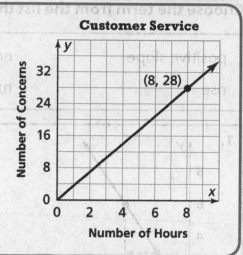

Customer Service

Number of Concerns

Number of Hours

Each week, the same amount of money is automatically taken
out of Geraldo's paycheck and deposited into his savings
account. This graph shows the relationship between the total
amount Geraldo has saved in dollars, y, to time in weeks, x.
Write the equation of the line that represents the relationship.

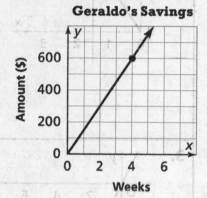

Geraldo's Savings

Amount ($)

Weeks

1. The graph starts at (0, 0). What other point is shown on
    the graph?

2. What are the rise and run between (0, 0) and the point you
    identified in Exercise 1?

3. What is the slope of the line?

4. Write the equation of the line.

On the Back!

5. Penny wrote the same number of holiday cards each day for 6 days,
    and she wrote a total of 42 cards. Graph the line relating the number
    of cards, y, to the number of days, x. Write the equation of the line that
    represents the relationship?

Name ______________________________

Choose the term from the list that best represents the item in each box.

positive slope	negative slope	constant of proportionality
rise	run	slope of the line

1.

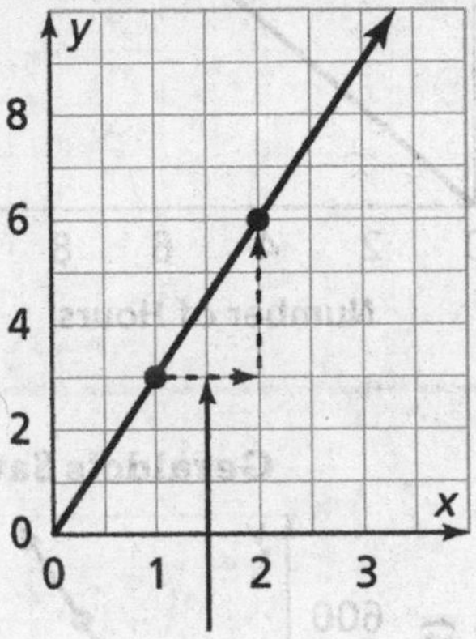

2.

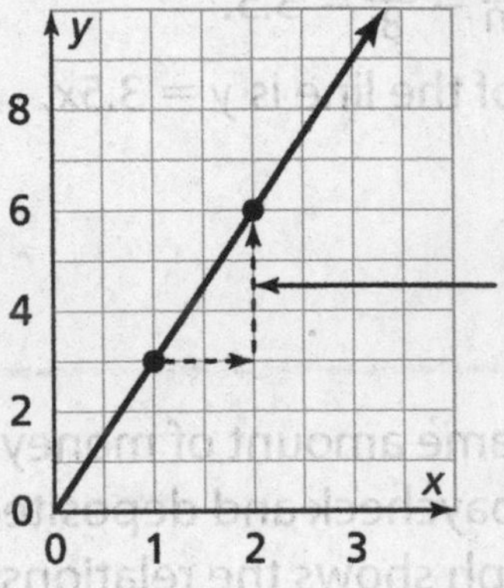

3.

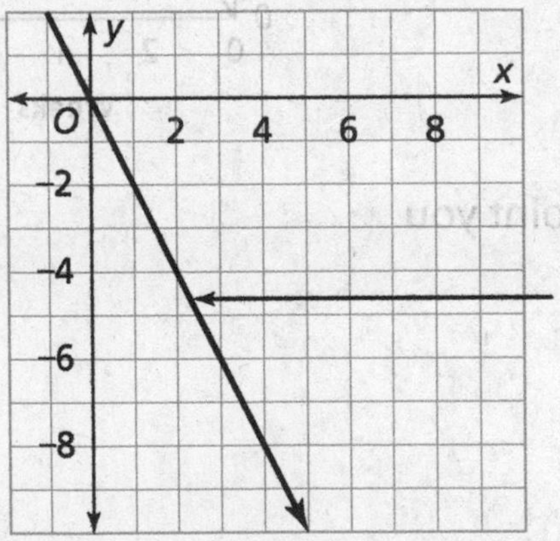

4.

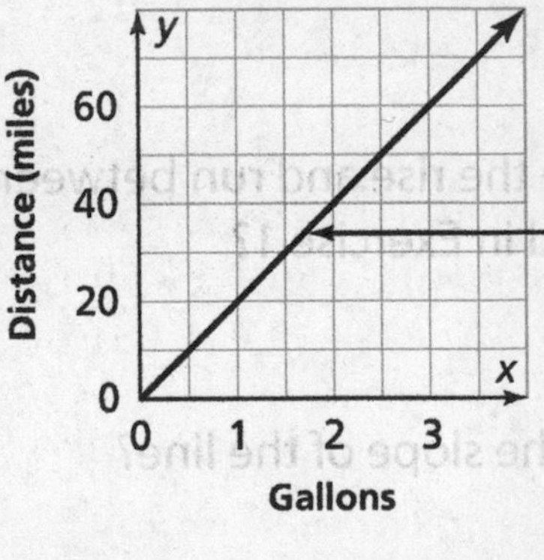
Distance per Gallon
Distance (miles)
Gallons

5. $y = kx$

6. $y = mx$

Name _____

Read the problem. Then answer the questions to help you write an equation.

The relationship between the distance traveled by an object moving at a constant speed, *y* and the hours, *x*, is shown in the graph. Write an equation that describes the relationship.

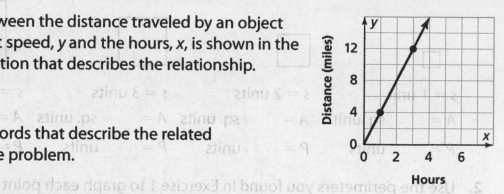

1. Highlight the words that describe the related quantities in the problem.

2. In what form is the equation of the line that describes the relationship? Explain.

3. What information do you need to find in order to write the equation? Explain.

4. Which point or points on the graph can you use to find the slope of the line? Explain.

1. For each square below, s represents the side length.
   Find the area A and the perimeter P of each square.

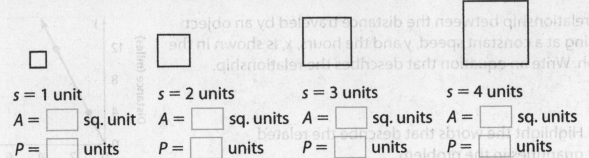

s = 1 unit
A = ☐ sq. unit
P = ☐ units

s = 2 units
A = ☐ sq. units
P = ☐ units

s = 3 units
A = ☐ sq. units
P = ☐ units

s = 4 units
A = ☐ sq. units
P = ☐ units

2. Use the perimeters you found in Exercise 1 to graph each point
   (s, P) on a line. Write an equation to describe the relationship
   between a square's side length and its perimeter. Use the slope to
   justify your answer.

3. Use the areas you found in Exercise 1 to graph each
   point (s, A). Do the points lie on a line? Use the slope
   to justify your answer.

4. What formula do you use to find the area of a square,
   A, when given its side length, s? Rewrite this formula by
   replacing s with x and A with y. Is this equation in the
   form $y = mx$? Explain.

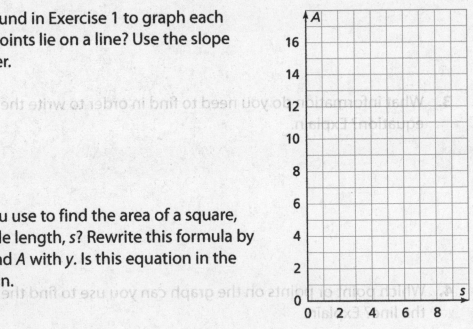

5. Which relationships are proportional? Select all that apply.

   ☐ The relationship between a square's side length and its perimeter

   ☐ The relationship between a square's side length and its area

Name _____

The *y*-intercept of a line is the *y*-coordinate of the point where the line crosses the *y*-axis.

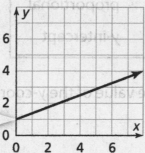

This line crosses the *y*-axis at (0, 1), so the *y*-intercept is 1.

In New York City, there is an initial fee for a daytime taxi plus a charge per mile traveled, as shown in the graph below. What is the *y*-intercept of the graph, and what does it represent?

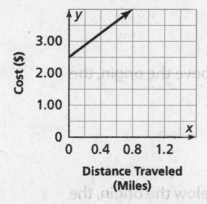

Distance Traveled (Miles)

1. At what point does the line cross the *y*-axis?

2. What is the *y*-intercept of the line?

3. The *y*-intercept gives the cost of a taxi for what distance traveled?

4. What does the *y*-intercept represent?

On the Back!

5. For a science experiment, Claudia observes the effects of temperature on a substance. The original temperature is 9°C, and Claudia increases the temperature by 2°C each hour. Then Claudia graphs the relationship between time and temperature. What is the *y*-intercept of Claudia's graph and what does it represent?

Use each of these terms once to complete the sentences.

negative	positive	proportional
y-axis	y-coordinate	y-intercept

1. The y-intercept of a line is the value of the y-coordinate where the line crosses the _____.

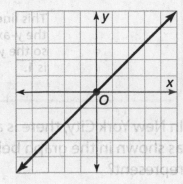

2. When the y-intercept of a line is 0, the relationship is _____.

3. When the graph of a line crosses above the origin, the y-intercept is _____.

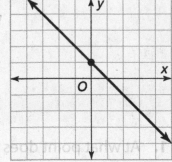

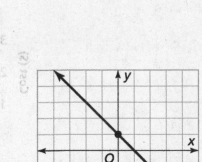

4. When the graph of a line crosses below the origin, the y-intercept is _____.

5. When the y-intercept of a line is positive, the _____ of the point is positive.

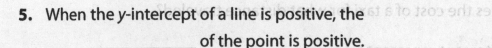

6. In the point (0, −1), −1 represents the _____.

Name _____

Read the problem. Then answer the questions to help you understand the problem.

A pump is removing water from a tank at a constant rate. The graph shows the relationship between the volume of water in the tank and the number of hours. What is the *y*-intercept of the graph, and what does it represent?

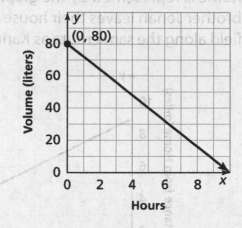

1. Underline each question you need to answer.

2. On the graph, circle the point that corresponds to the *y*-intercept. Explain how to use this point to find the *y*-intercept.

3. What does the graph show about how the volume of water in the tank changes over time?

4. Does the *y*-intercept represent a starting value or an ending value? Explain.

5. On the graph, highlight the information that describes the quantity represented on the *y*-axis. How does this help you determine the meaning of the *y*-intercept?

Karina leaves the soccer practice field to drive to her house, 9 miles away, at a speed of 30 miles per hour. Her distance from home is represented by the graph below. At the same time, her brother Jonah leaves their house and drives to the same practice field along the same route as Karina. His speed is 24 miles per hour.

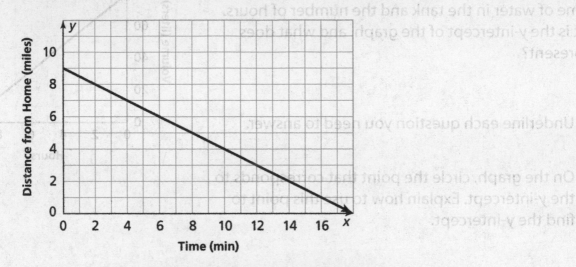

1. What are Karina's and Jonah's speeds in miles per minute?

2. Graph Jonah's distance from home on the axes above. What is the *y*-intercept of your graph and what does it represent?

3. Write an equation that represents Jonah's distance from home.

4. What is the *y*-intercept of the graph that represents Karina's distance from home and what does it represent?

5. At what point do the two graphs intersect, and what does this mean in terms of the situation?

6. Which graph represents a proportional relationship? Explain.

What is the equation of the line in slope-intercept form given its graph?

Step 1 Find *b*, the *y*-intercept.
The line crosses the *y*-axis at (0, 4),
so *b* = 4.

Step 2 Find *m*, the slope.
Two points on the line are (0, 4)
and (10, 6).
$\frac{rise}{run} = \frac{2}{10} = \frac{1}{5}$

Step 3 Write the equation *y* = *mx* + *b*.
$y = \frac{1}{5}x + 4$

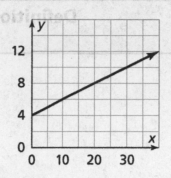

The line shows the cost for horseback riding at a local stable. What is the equation of the line in slope-intercept form?

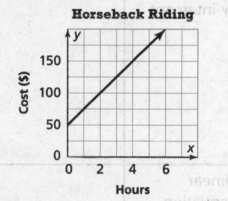

Horseback Riding

Cost ($)

Hours

1. You can write the equation in the form *y* = *mx* + *b*. What does *b* represent? What is the value of *b*?

2. What does *m* represent?

3. How can you use the line to find the value of *m*? What is the value of *m*?

4. What is the equation of the line?

On the Back!

5. Wally opened a savings account with a deposit of $100. He plans to put $40 each week into the account. What is the equation of the line in slope-intercept form that shows Wally's total savings?

Complete the vocabulary chart.

Word or Phrase	Definition	Picture or Example
slope		For the equation $y = -x + 2$, the slope is -1.
y-intercept		
linear equation		$y = -5x$ $y = 6x - 1$
slope-intercept form	The slope-intercept form of a linear equation is $y = mx + b$, where m represents the slope of the line and b represents the y-intercept of the line.	
linear equation of a proportional relationship		$y = 8x$ $y = -15x$

Answer the questions to help you understand characteristics of equations in the form of $y = mx$ and $y = mx + b$.

Characteristics of the Graph of the Equation	$y = mx$	$y = mx + b, b \neq 0$
Slope	m	m
y-intercept	0	b
$\dfrac{\text{change in } y}{\text{change in } x}$ is constant.	yes	yes
Shows a proportional relationship between x and y	yes	no

1. Circle the general forms of the equations of the lines shown in the table.

2. What information about slope is summarized in the table?

3. What information about the y-intercept is summarized in the table?

4. Why does the table have separate columns for the equations $y = mx$ and $y = mx + b$, where $b \neq 0$?

5. Write an equation that represents a proportional relationship when $m = 3$.

6. Write an equation that represents a relationship that is not proportional when $m = 3$ and $b = -6$.

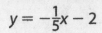

1. Graph the following equations on the coordinate plane at right.

   $y = -\frac{1}{5}x - 2$

   $y = x - 2$

   $y = 2x - 2$

   $y = -3x - 2$

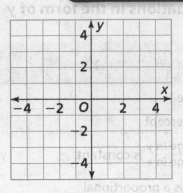

2. What do all of the equations in Exercise 1 have in common? How is this shown in the graphs?

3. Write an equation for another line that shares the property you described in Exercise 2.

4. Graph the following equations on the coordinate plane at right.

   $y = -\frac{1}{2}x + 3$

   $y = -\frac{1}{2}x$

   $y = -\frac{1}{2}x - 1$

   $y = -\frac{1}{2}x - 2$

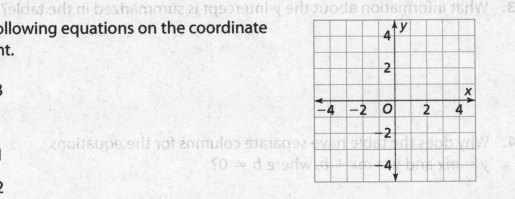

5. What do all of the equations in Exercise 4 have in common? How is this shown in the graphs?

6. Write an equation for a line that has each of the properties from Exercises 2 and 5.

Use Sampling to Draw Inferences About Populations

Dear Family,

Your child is analyzing surveys and other studies in which a population is sampled. He or she is learning to identify samples that are representative and to make inferences based on samples. Your child is also comparing sample data by using different types of data displays and measures such as mean, median, and mean absolute deviation.

You can help your child gain fluency with these topics by doing the following activity.

Evaluating Studies

Find an item or article about a recent survey or study. Possible resources are newspapers and magazines, television or radio news, or websites. Discuss the following questions with your child:

- What population is being studied?

- What sample is used to represent the population? Is the sample representative? Why or why not?

- What inferences does the study make about the population? Are the inferences valid? Why or why not?

Observe Your Child

Focus on Mathematical Practices

Construct viable arguments and critique the reasoning of others.

Help your child become proficient with this Mathematical Practice. Have your child suggest another way that the study's population could have been sampled, and explain why he or she thinks that method would produce a sample that better represents the population.

Nombre _____

Usar un muestreo para hacer inferencias sobre poblaciones

Estimada familia:

Su hijo o hija está analizando encuestas y otros estudios en los que se hace un muestreo de población. Está aprendiendo a identificar muestras representativas y a hacer inferencias a partir de muestras. También está usando diferentes tipos de representaciones de datos y mediciones, como la media, la mediana y la desviación absoluta media, para comparar datos muestrales.

Puede realizar la siguiente actividad para ayudar a su hijo o hija a adquirir fluidez en estos temas.

Evaluar estudios

Busque un artículo sobre una encuesta o un estudio que se haya realizado recientemente. Algunos posibles materiales de consulta son periódicos y revistas, noticias de televisión o de radio, o sitios Web. Comente con su hijo o hija las siguientes preguntas:

- ¿Qué población se estudia?

- ¿Qué muestra se usa para representar la población? ¿Es representativa la muestra? ¿Por qué?

- ¿Qué inferencias acerca de la población se hacen en el estudio? ¿Son válidas esas inferencias? ¿Por qué?

Observe a su hijo o hija

Enfoque en las Prácticas matemáticas
Construir argumentos viables y evaluar el razonamiento de otros.

Ayude a su hijo o hija a adquirir competencia en esta Práctica matemática. Pídale que sugiera otra forma de hacer un muestreo de la población del estudio, y que explique por qué cree que ese método generaría una muestra que representara mejor a la población.

A population is the entire collection of people, items, or events that you want to study. A sample is a subset of people, items, or events from the larger population.

A representative sample of a population accurately reflects the characteristics or preferences of the entire population.

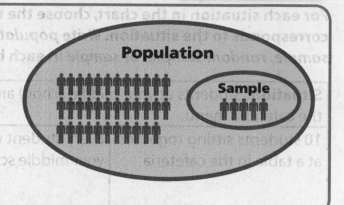

Walter wants to learn more about the preferred salad ingredients of students in his school. He surveys all students in his math class and finds that 4 prefer tomatoes, 14 prefer carrots, and 9 prefer cucumbers. What is the population and sample? Is the sample a representative sample? Explain.

1. The population is the entire group of people that Walter is studying. What is the population Walter wants to study?

2. Add the numbers of responses to determine the sample.

   The sample is ☐ + ☐ + ☐ = ☐ students in Walter's math class.

3. Think about whether Walter's sample accurately reflects the entire population. Is Walter's sample representative? Explain.

On the Back!

4. Guillermo randomly surveys 15 members of his community service group to gain ideas for the next community service project. What is the population of this study?

For each situation in the chart, choose the term that best corresponds to the situation. Write *population, representative sample, random sample,* **or** *sample* **in each box. Answers may vary.**

Situation: Students at your middle school are surveyed about their favorite beverage on the cafeteria menu.		
10 students sitting together at a table in the cafeteria	Every student who attends your middle school	10 students whose names are chosen from a hat, without looking, that contains a number of tickets equal to the school's population, each one labeled with a student's name

Situation: The mayor of your town wants to know if residents will vote to build a new library.		
All town voters	50 town residents who are voters	50 residents whose children attend public schools in the town

Situation: A newspaper wants to identify a city's favorite museum.		
Residents who are randomly selected from the city census	Visitors at the science museum on Friday night	All the residents of the city

Name _____

Visitors at a library were surveyed about their favorite types of fiction from the three choices shown. How many visitors responded to this survey? What could have been the population studied?

Favorite Type of Fiction	Number of Votes
Mystery	21
Science Fiction	15
Romance	14

1. What information is described in the table?

2. The problem asks two questions. Underline the question that you can answer with the information given in the table.

3. How will you use the information in the table to answer the underlined question?

4. Circle the word or phrase that can help you answer the other question. Explain why this information is useful.

The manager of a cinema with multiple theaters randomly surveyed customers about whether they would prefer to view a new movie in a regular or a 3-D theater. The manager recorded the survey results in the table.

1. Out of a group of 500 customers, every 10th customer is chosen to participate in the survey. Complete the table to describe how many respondents would prefer to view the movie in a 3-D theater.

Do You Prefer Regular or 3-D?

Type of Theater	Number
Regular	30
3-D	

2. Suppose the manager surveyed every 10th customer who viewed a movie at the cinema on a Sunday afternoon. Is this a representative sample? Justify your answer.

3. Suppose a population of customers contains 100 adults and 25 children. If a representative sample from this population contains 12 adults, how many children should the sample contain? Explain.

4. Suppose a representative sample contains 40 weekday customers and 80 weekend customers. If the population contains 400 weekday customers, what is the total number of customers in the population? Explain.

5. The manager wants to learn more about the preferences of customers who go to the movies on Friday nights. Describe how a representative sample can be obtained.

The band director asked 10 randomly selected band members whether they would prefer an extra rehearsal on Tuesday, Wednesday, or Thursday. Based on her sample, estimate how many of the 40 total band members would prefer to rehearse on Tuesday.

Tuesday	5
Wednesday	2
Thursday	3

5 of the 10 members in the sample prefer Tuesday.

$$\frac{5}{10} = \frac{x}{40}$$

$$\frac{5}{10} \cdot 40 = \frac{x}{40} \cdot 40$$

$$20 = x$$

Let x represent the number of the 40 total band members who prefer Tuesday.

Based on the sample, about 20 band members would be expected to prefer to have an extra rehearsal on Tuesday.

Mr. Seratelli is the principal of a school with 280 students. He surveys 70 randomly selected students to learn more about where they would like to spend recess. Based on the sample, estimate how many of the students at Mr. Seratelli's school would like to spend recess in the gym.

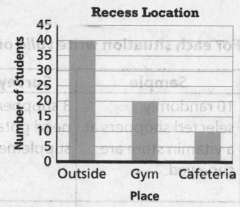

Recess Location

(bar graph: y-axis "Number of Students" from 0 to 45, x-axis "Place" with Outside ≈ 40, Gym ≈ 20, Cafeteria ≈ 10)

1. Fill in the boxes to write a proportion. Use x to represent the unknown value.

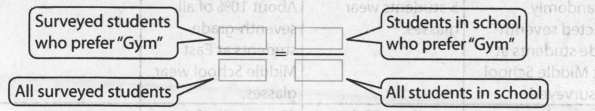

Surveyed students who prefer "Gym"

Students in school who prefer "Gym"

$$\frac{\boxed{}}{\boxed{}} = \frac{\boxed{}}{\boxed{}}$$

All surveyed students

All students in school

2. To solve the proportion from Exercise 1, by what number are both sides of the proportion multiplied?

3. Solve the proportion from Exercise 1. Based on the sample, estimate how many students at the school would prefer to spend recess in the gym.

On the Back!

4. On a school bus trip, 15 out of 25 randomly selected students would like to stop for lunch. There are 55 students on the bus. Based on the sample data, estimate the number of students on the bus who would like to stop for lunch.

Use the words in the list to complete the sentences below.

inference	invalid	valid

1. A(n) _____ is a judgment made by interpreting data.

2. An inference that is based on a representative sample is _____.

3. An inference that does not represent the population is _____.

For each situation write *valid* or *invalid*.

Sample	Survey Results	Inference	Valid or Invalid?
10 randomly selected shoppers at a vitamin store are surveyed.	3 shoppers need potassium supplements.	About 30% of all people need potassium supplements.	
50 randomly selected seventh-grade students at East Middle School are surveyed.	5 students wear glasses.	About 10% of all seventh-grade students at East Middle School wear glasses.	
5 randomly selected students in a homeroom try to wiggle their ears.	2 students in the sample can wiggle their ears.	About 40% of the students in the homeroom can wiggle their ears.	
20 randomly selected cell phones from one shipment are tested.	1 cell phone in the sample is defective.	About 5% of all cell phones are defective.	

Three farm workers collected data about three different samples of 50 cartons of eggs randomly selected from a total shipment of 500 cartons. The tables below show the numbers of cartons with cracked eggs and with no cracked eggs in each sample. What inference can be made about the number of cartons with cracked eggs in the entire shipment?

Sample 1	
Cracked Eggs	11
No Cracked Eggs	39

Sample 2	
Cracked Eggs	12
No Cracked Eggs	38

Sample 3	
Cracked Eggs	9
No Cracked Eggs	41

1. Describe in your own words what the problem is asking you to do.

2. What do the numbers in the tables represent?

3. What is the sum of the two numbers in each table? Why does this make sense?

4. For Sample 1, you can write and solve the proportion $\frac{11}{50} = \frac{x}{500}$. What do the three numbers and the variable x in this proportion represent?

Name _____

In a town of 10,000 people, four surveys were conducted to determine whether the residents want a new skate park. The diagrams describe the samples and results of each survey, and valid and invalid inferences are stated below the diagrams. Using the given information, write a number from the list below in each box to complete the diagram and inference statements. Use each number only once.

$\frac{1}{40}$	$\frac{1}{4}$	4	25	100	1,000

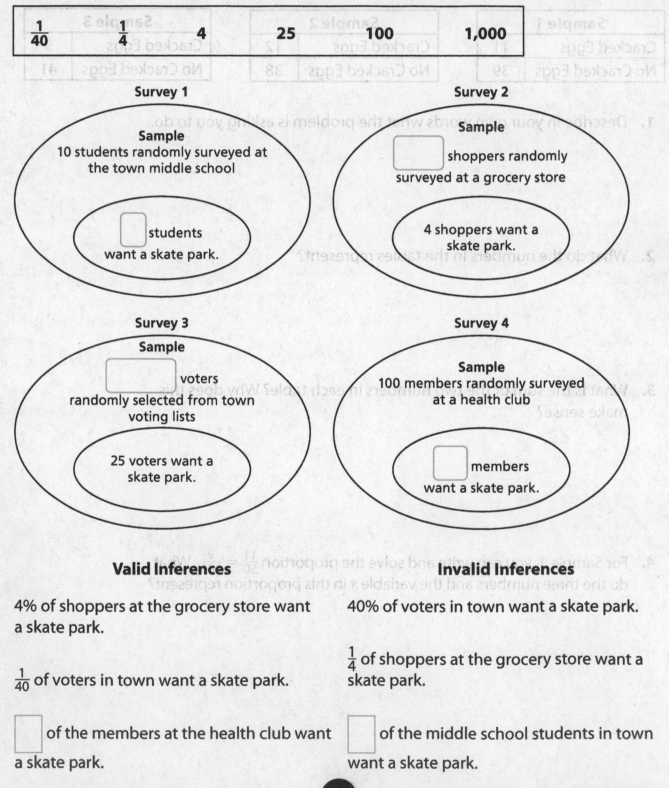

Survey 1

Sample
10 students randomly surveyed at the town middle school

☐ students want a skate park.

Survey 2

Sample
☐ shoppers randomly surveyed at a grocery store

4 shoppers want a skate park.

Survey 3

Sample
☐ voters randomly selected from town voting lists

25 voters want a skate park.

Survey 4

Sample
100 members randomly surveyed at a health club

☐ members want a skate park.

Valid Inferences

4% of shoppers at the grocery store want a skate park.

$\frac{1}{40}$ of voters in town want a skate park.

☐ of the members at the health club want a skate park.

Invalid Inferences

40% of voters in town want a skate park.

$\frac{1}{4}$ of shoppers at the grocery store want a skate park.

☐ of the middle school students in town want a skate park.

E 8-2

The following box plots describe the amounts of time spent doing homework last night by seventh-graders in two homerooms.

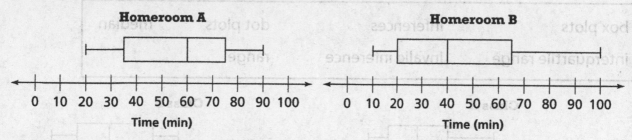

The median for Homeroom A, 60 minutes, is greater than the median for Homeroom B, 40 minutes, so students in Homeroom A generally spent more time on homework as compared to students in Homeroom B.

The interquartile range for Homeroom B, 45, is greater than the interquartile range for Homeroom A, 40. So, there is greater variability, or spread, among the amounts of time spent on homework by students in Homeroom B.

Teachers and students were asked how many movies they had seen during the last year. Use the median to make a comparative inference about the data.

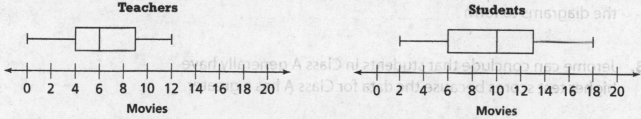

1. What is the median number of movies seen by the teachers?

2. What is the median number of movies seen by the students?

3. Which data set has the greater median?

4. Use the median to make a comparative inference about the data.

On the Back!

5. Use the interquartile range to make a comparative inference about the movie data for teachers and students shown above.

Use the words and phrases once to complete the sentences below.
Some words or phrases might not be used at all.

box plots	inferences	dot plots	median
interquartile range	invalid inference	range	

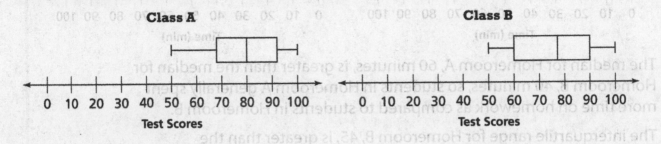

Class A

Class B

0 10 20 30 40 50 60 70 80 90 100
Test Scores

0 10 20 30 40 50 60 70 80 90 100
Test Scores

1. The diagrams that describe test scores for students in two classes at Jerome's school are called _____.

2. Jerome can use the data about Class A and Class B described in the diagrams to form _____.

3. Jerome can conclude that students in Class A generally have higher test scores because the data for Class A has a greater _____.

4. The difference between the highest and lowest scores for each class is the same, so the data for both Class A and Class B have the same _____.

5. Jerome can conclude that the there is greater variation, or spread, of the scores for Class B because these data have a greater _____.

6. Each set of data starts at 50 and ends at 100, so Jerome concludes that both classes include the same number of test scores. This conclusion is a(n) _____.

Name _____

The following box plots describe the amounts of time students take
to solve the same puzzle. How do the two populations compare?
What inferences can be made about the amounts of time taken?

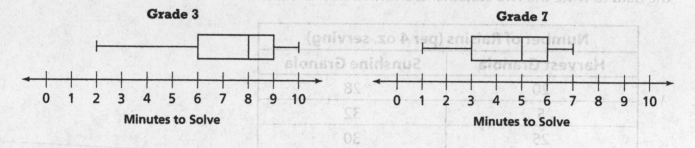

Grade 3

Minutes to Solve

Grade 7

Minutes to Solve

1. Describe in your own words what the problem is asking you to do.

2. What statistical value is represented by the vertical line in the
    middle of the box in each box plot?

3. In the box plot for Grade 3, there are short vertical lines at 2 and 10.
    Explain the meaning of these short vertical lines.

4. What statistical value is represented by the length of the box in
    each data set??

5. Describe how these data can be compared to form valid inferences.

An advertising agency collected data on the number of raisins in five different servings of Harvest Granola and Sunshine Granola. The agency recorded the data in the tables shown, and then used the data to write the two statements shown below the tables.

| Number of Raisins (per 4 oz. serving) ||
Harvest Granola	Sunshine Granola
20	28
5	32
25	30
26	26
24	34

Statement A
Sunshine Granola has 50% more raisins than Harvest Granola.

Statement B
Harvest Granola has 20% fewer raisins than Sunshine Granola.

1. Which statistical measure of center can be used to justify Statement A? Explain.

2. Which statistical measure of center can be used to justify Statement B? Explain.

3. Do you think an advertisement containing Statement A would be misleading? Explain.

4. Do you think an advertisement containing Statement B would be misleading? Explain.

5. Which statement do you think would be more effective in an advertisement? Explain.

Name _____

One week, Margaret drove to work. The next week, she rode the train. Each day, she recorded how long it took in minutes. What can Margaret infer from the two data sets?

Travel Times (minutes)					
Drive	40	36	50	44	50
Train	36	44	46	42	44

Display the two data sets in dot plots.

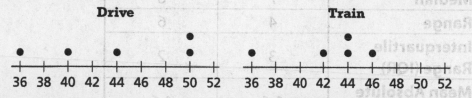

Drive

36 38 40 42 44 46 48 50 52

Train

36 38 40 42 44 46 48 50 52

The driving data has a mean of 44 and a MAD of 4.8. The train data has a mean of 42.4 and a MAD of 2.72. Based on these data, Margaret can infer that driving generally takes longer and is less consistent than taking the train to work.

The table at right describes the prices of several homes in the towns of Cali and Barton. What can you infer from the mean and MAD of the two data sets?

Home Prices (thousands of dollars)					
Cali	100	200	175	150	175
Barton	75	225	100	175	100

1. Complete the dot plots to describe the home prices in each town.

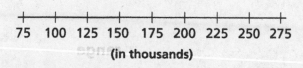

Home Prices in Cali

75 100 125 150 175 200 225 250 275
(in thousands)

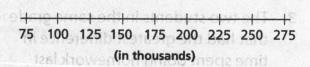

Home Prices in Barton

75 100 125 150 175 200 225 250 275
(in thousands)

2. What can you infer from the MAD of the two data sets?

On the Back!

3. In the table above, suppose the price of the $225,000 home in Barton is reduced to $150,000. How would this affect the relationship between the means of the data sets?

Students in Grade 6 and Grade 8 were asked how many hours they spent doing homework last week. Data recorded from responses of 30 students in each grade are recorded in the table below.

	Grade 6	Grade 8
Mean	6	8
Median	7	8
Range	4	6
Interquartile Range (IQR)	3	2
Mean Absolute Deviation (MAD)	1.6	1.6

Match each inference with the statistical measure that best justifies the inference.

1. The middle two quartiles of students in Grade 6 had greater variability in time spent doing homework last week than the middle two quartiles of students in Grade 8.

mean

2. On average, students in Grade 8 spent 2 more hours last week doing homework than students in Grade 6.

median

3. The two students in the same grade that had the greatest difference in time spent doing homework last week are in Grade 8.

range

4. The general variability of values from the average is the same in each grade.

interquartile range (IQR)

5. Half of the students in Grade 8 spent more time doing homework last week than at least half of the students in Grade 6.

mean absolute deviation (MAD)

Name _____

The following table shows the lengths of time taken by two different school buses to complete their morning routes on the same 7 days. Find the median and range of each set of data and compare the lengths of time taken by the different school buses.

Number of Minutes to Complete the Morning Route	
Bus A	**Bus B**
90	70
80	50
90	90
70	60
90	80
80	80
70	60

1. Underline the statistical measures you must calculate in order to solve this problem. Once you have calculated these measures, will you have completed the problem? Explain.

2. Draw a circle around each data set. How many values are in each set?

3. The last row of the table contains the values 70 and 60. What are the real-world meanings of these values?

4. What inferences can be made by comparing the median and the range of these sets of data?

The table at right describes the results of a survey taken by five students in Grade 4, five students in Grade 6, and five students in Grade 8.

Time Spent on Homework (hours per week)		
Grade 4	**Grade 6**	**Grade 8**
6	4	9
3	7	7
7	8	11
6	4	8
3	7	5

1. For each grade level, the mean absolute deviation (MAD) of the data is 1.6. Find the mean of the data for each grade.

2. Complete the table by finding the difference between the means for Grades 4 and 6 and for Grades 6 and 8. Then, express each difference between means as a multiple of the MAD.

	Grades 4 and 6	**Grades 6 and 8**
Difference Between Means	☐ − ☐ = ☐	☐ − ☐ = ☐
Number of Multiples of MAD = difference between means / MAD	☐/☐ = ☐	☐/☐ = ☐

3. Use the number lines below to create a dot plot for each pair of grades. Use solid dots for Grade 4, open dots for Grade 6, and striped dots for Grade 8.

Time Spent on Homework Grades 4 and 6

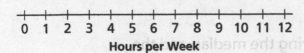

0 1 2 3 4 5 6 7 8 9 10 11 12
Hours per Week

Time Spent on Homework Grades 6 and 8

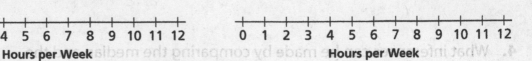

0 1 2 3 4 5 6 7 8 9 10 11 12
Hours per Week

4. When the difference between means is a greater multiple of the MAD, does the dot plot show more or less visual overlap between the data sets?

Name _____

Probability

Dear Family,

   Your child is studying probabilities of simple and compound events. He or she is learning to use precise terms to describe actions and their possible outcomes, and to distinguish between and determine theoretical and experimental probabilities.
   You can help your child understand probability concepts by playing the following game.

Number Cube Probability

Materials: Number cube, paper, and pencil for each player

Step 1 Each player lists three possible events when rolling a number cube:

   - An event with probability $\frac{1}{6}$, such as "2"
   - An event with probability $\frac{1}{3}$, such as "5 or 6"
   - An event with probability $\frac{1}{2}$, such as "odd number"

Step 2 Player 1 rolls the number cube. If the result matches an event from Player 1's list, he or she places a check mark next to that event. A player may check no more than one event per turn.

Step 3 Players take turns rolling the number cube until one player has checked all three events on his or her list.

Observe Your Child

Focus on Mathematical Practices
Construct viable arguments and critique the reasoning of others.

Help your child become proficient with this Mathematical Practice. Ask him or her to develop and explain a strategy for choosing events in Step 1. Consider playing the game several times to allow your child to use and compare different strategies.

Probabilidad

Estimada familia:

Su hijo o hija está estudiando probabilidades de eventos simples y compuestos. Está aprendiendo a usar términos precisos para describir acciones y los resultados posibles de esas acciones, y a determinar y distinguir entre probabilidades teóricas y experimentales.

Puede ayudar a su hijo o hija a comprender conceptos relacionados con la probabilidad jugando el siguiente juego.

Probabilidad con un cubo numérico

Materiales: Cubo numérico, papel y lápiz para cada jugador

Paso 1 Cada jugador hace una lista de tres eventos posibles que resulten de lanzar un cubo numérico:

- Un evento con una probabilidad de $\frac{1}{6}$; por ejemplo, "2"

- Un evento con una probabilidad de $\frac{1}{3}$; por ejemplo, "5 o 6"

- Un evento con una probabilidad de $\frac{1}{2}$; por ejemplo, "número impar"

Paso 2 El Jugador 1 lanza el cubo numérico. Si el resultado coincide con un evento de su lista, traza una marca junto a ese evento. Los jugadores no deben marcar más de un evento en cada turno.

Paso 3 Los jugadores se turnan para lanzar el cubo numérico hasta que un jugador haya marcado los tres eventos de su lista.

Observe a su hijo o hija

Enfoque en las Prácticas matemáticas
Construir argumentos viables y evaluar el razonamiento de otros.

Ayude a su hijo o hija a adquirir competencia en esta Práctica matemática. Pídale que formule y explique una estrategia para escoger los eventos del Paso 1. Pueden jugar el juego varias veces para que su hijo o hija tenga la posibilidad de aplicar y comparar diferentes estrategias.

A box contains 8 equal-sized tiles labeled *A, A, A, A, B, B, C* and *D.* Jonah will randomly select one tile from the box. What is the probability that Jonah will select a tile labeled with the letter *B*? Describe this probability as *impossible, unlikely, neither likely nor unlikely, likely,* or *certain.*

A	A	A	A
B	B	C	D

There are 8 tiles. Two of the tiles have the letter *B.*

The probability is 2 out of 8; $\frac{2}{8} = \frac{1}{4}$.

It is unlikely that Jonah will select a tile labeled with the letter *B.*

A bag contains 5 green marbles and 2 purple marbles. Keisha will randomly select one marble from the bag. What is the probability that Keisha will select a green marble? Describe this probability as *impossible, unlikely, neither likely nor unlikely, likely,* or *certain.*

1. How many marbles are in the bag?

2. The probability that Keisha will select a green marble is ☐ out of ☐ .

3. What is the probability that Keisha will select a green marble?

   ☐
   ─
   ☐

4. It is ☐ that Keisha will select a green marble.

On the Back!

5. A bag contains 10 black tiles and 10 white tiles. Caden will randomly select one tile from the bag. What is the probability that Caden will select a black tile? Describe this probability as *impossible, unlikely, neither likely nor unlikely, likely,* or *certain.*

Cards are selected randomly from the set of 10 cards shown below.

| 1 | 2 | 2 | 4 | 5 | 5 | 5 | 7 | 8 | 8 |

Use terms from the list below to complete the sentences.

| probability | outcome | equally likely |

1. Selecting a card with an even number is an example of a(n)

   _____.

2. The _____ that a card with a 5 will be randomly
   selected can be written as three out of ten, or $\frac{3}{10}$.

3. Selecting a card labeled with an even number and selecting a card
   labeled with an odd number are _____.

Circle *impossible*, *unlikely*, *likely*, or *certain* for each event.

4. Randomly selecting a card labeled with a number greater than 3

   impossible   unlikely   likely   certain

5. Randomly selecting a card labeled with a number less than 10

   impossible   unlikely   likely   certain

6. Randomly selecting a card labeled with the number 1

   impossible   unlikely   likely   certain

7. Randomly selecting a card labeled with a number greater than 8

   impossible   unlikely   likely   certain

Name _____

Read the problem below. Then answer the questions to understand the problem.

Kendall designed this spinner for a contest. All sections of this spinner are equal in size. Did Kendall design a fair spinner? If yes, explain why it is a fair spinner. If not, explain how to make it a fair spinner.

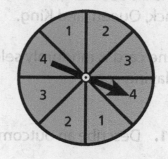

1. Circle the question you need to answer.

2. What does it mean for the spinner to be "fair"?

3. How many sections does the spinner have? Underline the sentence in the problem that gives important information about the sections. What does this sentence tell you about the chance for the pointer to land in each section?

4. Use different colors to highlight the numbers on the spinner that are the same. How many times does each number appear?

5. After you have determined whether the spinner is fair, will you have completely solved the problem? Explain.

There are 52 playing cards in a standard deck. Each card is
assigned to one of four suits: diamonds, hearts, spades, or clubs.
Within each suit, there are 13 ranks: Ace, 2, 3, 4, 5, 6, 7, 8, 9, 10,
Jack, Queen, and King.

One card is randomly selected from a standard deck of
playing cards.

1. Describe an outcome that is certain. Explain.

2. Suppose the card selected is assigned to the diamonds suit.
Describe a different outcome that is equally likely.

3. For which outcome below is the probability equal to $\frac{1}{13}$? Circle this
outcome. Explain.

Selecting a King   Selecting a heart   Selecting the King of hearts

4. Suppose you are unaware that the 9 of clubs is missing from the deck.

a. Describe an event that is less likely than may be expected. Explain.

b. Describe an event that is more likely than may be expected. Explain.

c. Describe an event that is equally likely, regardless of the missing card. Explain.

Out of 300 spins, how many times is the pointer of the spinner expected to land on Win?

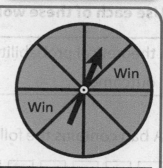

Step 1 Find the possible outcomes of one spin. There are 8 equal-sized sections, so there are 8 possible outcomes.	Step 2 Find the theoretical probability that the pointer will land on Win. $P(\text{Win}) = \dfrac{\text{number of Win sections}}{\text{total number of sections}}$ $\dfrac{2}{8} = \dfrac{1}{4}$	Step 3 Use proportional reasoning to predict the likely number of winning spins, w. $\dfrac{1}{4} = \dfrac{w}{300}$ $\dfrac{1}{4} \cdot 300 = \dfrac{w}{300} \cdot 300$ $75 = w$

Out of 300 spins, you can expect the pointer to land on Win about 75 times.

On how many out of 200 spins do you expect the pointer to land on Win?

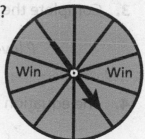

1. How many equal-sized sections does this spinner have?

2. Find the theoretical probability that the pointer will land on Win.

$P(\text{Win}) = \dfrac{\text{number of Win sections}}{\text{total number of sections}} = \dfrac{\Box}{\Box} = \dfrac{1}{\Box}$

3. Complete the proportion to find the number of expected wins, w, in 200 spins.

$\dfrac{\Box}{\Box} = \dfrac{w}{\Box}$

4. On how many out of 200 spins do you expect the pointer to land on Win?

On the Back!

5. Of 8 equal-sized sections on a spinner, 3 are shaded green. On how many out of 400 spins do you expect the pointer to land in a green section?

Use each of these words or phrases once to complete the sentences below.

theoretical probability	events	favorable outcomes
outcome	likely	unlikely

A bag contains the following lettered tiles.

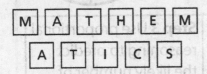

1. A tile is randomly selected from the bag. The expressions "the tile shows a vowel" and "the tile shows the letter *S*" are examples of

   _____ .

2. The tile chosen from the bag shows the letter *T*. This letter is a possible

   _____ of randomly choosing a tile.

3. Complete the following equation:

   $$P \text{ (event)} = \frac{\text{number of } \boxed{}}{\text{total number of possible outcomes}}$$

4. The equation from Exercise 3 can be used to determine the

   _____ of an event.

5. The probability of choosing a tile that shows the letter *E* is

   _____ .

6. The probability of choosing a tile that shows a consonant is

   _____ .

Read the problem below. Then answer the questions to understand the problem.

Contestants play a game at a neighborhood fair by spinning the pointer of a spinner with five equal-sized sections. A contestant wins if the pointer lands in section 3. How many winners are expected if 200 people play the game?

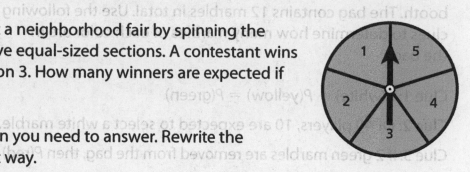

1. Underline the question you need to answer. Rewrite the question in a different way.

2. Highlight the word or words in the problem that provide important information about the sections. Why is this information important?

3. What information is given by the diagram?

4. For what event must the theoretical probability be determined to solve this problem?

5. Once you have found the theoretical probability, will you have solved the problem? Explain.

A blindfolded contestant makes a random selection from a bag
that contains white, red, green, and yellow marbles at a carnival
booth. The bag contains 12 marbles in total. Use the following
clues to determine how many marbles of each color are in
the bag.

Clue 1: $P(\text{white}) + P(\text{yellow}) = P(\text{green})$

Clue 2: Of 40 players, 10 are expected to select a white marble.

Clue 3: If 2 green marbles are removed from the bag, then $P(\text{red}) = \frac{1}{5}$.

1. How many white marbles are in the bag? Explain.

2. How many red marbles are in the bag? Explain.

3. How many marbles are yellow or green? Explain.

4. Each probability in this equation can be written as a fraction
whose denominator is 12. Let y represent the number of yellow
marbles and let g represent the number of green marbles in the
bag. According to Clue 1, $P(\text{white}) + P(\text{yellow}) = P(\text{green})$. Write the
numerators of the fractions in the boxes below.

$$P(\text{white}) + P(\text{yellow}) = P(\text{green})$$
$$\downarrow \qquad\qquad \downarrow \qquad\qquad \downarrow$$
$$\frac{\boxed{}}{12} + \frac{\boxed{}}{12} = \frac{\boxed{}}{12}$$

5. Use your answer from Exercise 3 and the equation from Exercise 4 to
determine the numbers of yellow and green marbles in the bag.

Name _____

A spinner has 8 equal-sized sections. Four of the sections are blue, two are red, and two are green. The pointer lands in a red section 8 times in 20 spins. How does this compare to the number of times the pointer is expected to land in a red section?

Step 1 Use the experiment's results to find the experimental probability that the pointer lands in a red section.

$$\text{Experimental probability} = \frac{\text{number of times pointer lands in a red section}}{\text{total number of spins}} = \frac{8}{20} = 40\%$$

Step 2 Find the theoretical probability that the pointer lands in a red section.

$$P(\text{red}) = \frac{\text{number of red sections}}{\text{total number of equal-sized sections}} = \frac{2}{8} = 25\%$$

The experimental probability is greater than the theoretical probability. The pointer landed in a red section more often than expected.

A spinner has 10 equal-sized sections labeled 1 through 10. In 40 spins, the spinner lands 3 times in section 5. How does this compare to the number of times the pointer is expected to land in section 5?

1. Find the experimental probability that the pointer lands in section 5.

$$\frac{\text{number of times pointer lands in section 5}}{\text{total number of spins}} = \frac{\square}{\square} = \boxed{}\%$$

2. Find the theoretical probability that the pointer lands in section 5.

$$P(5) = \frac{\text{number of sections labeled "5"}}{\text{total number of equal-sized sections}} = \frac{\square}{\square} = \boxed{}\%$$

3. How does the actual number of times the pointer landed in section 5 compare to the expected number?

On the Back!

4. A spinner has 4 equal-sized sections labeled 1 through 4. In 25 spins, the spinner lands 5 times in section 3. How does this compare to the number of times the pointer is expected to land in section 3?

The table below compares two types of probability. Use terms from the list below to complete the top three rows of the table. You may need to use some terms more than once. Then describe an example of each type of probability in the bottom row.

event	outcomes	Experimental Probability
Theoretical Probability	trials	relative frequency

Probability Type		
Description	This probability is found by counting desired and possible _____ .	This probability is found by conducting _____ in which an action is conducted multiple times. This probability may also be called the _____ of an event.
Ratio	$\dfrac{\text{number of favorable } _____}{\text{total number of possible } _____}$	$\dfrac{\text{number of times } _____ \text{ occurs}}{\text{total number of } _____}$
Example		

Read the problem below. Then answer the questions to understand the problem.

Mary and Nyla are playing a game. They each spin the pointer of the spinner shown at right 100 times. The results after 40 spins for each player are recorded in the tables below.

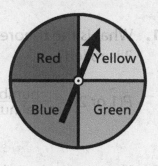

Mary	
Red	9
Yellow	12
Green	9
Blue	10

Nyla	
Red	11
Yellow	10
Green	11
Blue	8

a. Based on theoretical probability, what are the expected results of 100 spins?

b. Should Mary and Nyla expect the same results after 100 spins? Explain.

c. Why might their results be different from the expected results based on theoretical probability?

1. How many questions must be answered to completely solve this problem? Underline each question.

2. What data are represented by the numbers in the tables?

3. Circle the first number in each table. What do these numbers represent in this problem situation?

4. What information is provided by the diagram? Why is this information important?

Use a cube with sides numbered 1 through 6 to answer the following questions.

1. What is the theoretical probability that a number less than 3 is rolled?

$$P(1 \text{ or } 2) = \frac{\text{number of favorable outcomes}}{\text{total number of possible outcomes}} = \frac{\square}{\square} = \frac{\square}{\square}$$

2. How many times is it expected that a number less than 3 will be rolled in 3 trials? 12 trials? 30 trials?

3. Roll the number cube 3 times and record the results. How many times did you roll a number less than 3? Use your experimental probability to predict the number of times you will roll a number less than 3 in the next 12 trials.

4. Roll the number cube 12 times and record the results. How many times did you roll a number less than 3? Use your experimental probability to predict the number of times you will roll a number less than 3 in the next 30 trials.

5. Roll the number cube 30 times and record the results. How many times did you roll a number less than 3?

6. Compare your results from Exercise 5 with your predictions based on theoretical probability in Exercise 2 and with your predictions based on experimental probability in Exercises 3 and 4. Which predictions were more accurate? Explain.

Omar randomly selects a marble from
the jar shown.

Omar can develop a probability model
based on theoretical probability.

G represents a green marble.
Y represents a yellow marble.
R represents a red marble.

A probability model consists of the
sample space and a list of events
within the sample space with their probabilities.

The sample space, S, is the set of all possible outcomes.

$$S = \{G, G, G, R, R, Y, Y, Y, Y, Y, Y, Y\}$$

The probabilities of all possible events in the sample space are described below.

Drawing a green marble: $P(G) = \frac{3}{12} = \frac{1}{4}$

Drawing a yellow marble: $P(Y) = \frac{7}{12}$

Drawing a red marble: $P(R) = \frac{2}{12} = \frac{1}{6}$

Ashley collects colored golf balls from a miniature golf course. She will
randomly select one ball from her collection of 9 blue, 7 magenta, and 2 purple
golf balls. Develop a probability model based on theoretical probability.

1. What is the total number of colored golf balls in Ashley's collection?

2. What is the sample space?
   $S =$

3. What is the theoretical probability that each event in the
   sample space occurs?

On the Back!

4. Hannah selects a marble randomly from a jar containing 11 green,
   5 yellow, and 4 red marbles. Develop a probability model based on
   theoretical probability.

Name _____

A marble is randomly selected from a box containing 12 marbles as described below:

- 1 black
- 3 green
- 4 red
- 2 yellow
- 2 purple

Draw lines to match each item in Column A to the corresponding item in Column B.

Column A

Column B

selecting a yellow marble; selecting a purple marble

possible event

$S = \{B, G, G, G, R, R, R, R, Y, Y, P, P\}$

probability model

selecting a green marble

equally likely

the probability of selecting a black marble

impossible event

sample space of events including all corresponding events with their probabilities

sample space

selecting a white marble

$P(B) = \dfrac{1}{12}$

Read the problem below. Then answer the questions to understand the problem.

A jar contains 250 marbles. A marble is randomly selected from the jar and replaced after its color is recorded. Based on the results of 100 random selections shown in the table below, how many marbles of each color are expected to be the jar?

Color	Red	Blue	Yellow	Green
Number of Marbles Selected	28	24	32	16

1. What information will a complete answer to this problem contain?

2. Underline the questions you need to answer. What does the word "expected" tell you about your answer?

3. Circle the numbers in the problem and in the table. Describe any relationships among the numbers.

4. This problem can be solved by developing a probability model. Will the probability model be based on theoretical or experimental probability? Explain.

5. What is the sample space?

6. Let g represent the expected number of green marbles in the jar. Circle the proportion you can use to find g.

$$\frac{16}{250} = \frac{g}{100} \qquad \frac{16}{100} = \frac{g}{250} \qquad \frac{16}{81} = \frac{g}{100} \qquad \frac{16}{250} = \frac{g}{81}$$

Of all the 6 students on the Math Olympiad team, 3 members are seventh-grade students and 3 are eighth-grade students. The coach will place equal-sized tickets labeled A7, B7, C7, D8, E8, and F8 to represent each team member in a hat and randomly select two tickets to choose the team captains.

1. Write the sample space of all possible pairs of students. How many pairings are possible?

2. What is the probability that both team captains will be seventh-grade students? Explain.

3. Jamal, one of the team members in seventh grade, wonders about the probability that he and another seventh-grade student will be selected. Is this probability equal to the probability determined in Exercise 2? Explain.

4. Samantha is one of the team members in eighth grade. She wonders about the probability that she and another eighth-grade student will be chosen as team captains. Explain why this is equal to the probability determined in Exercise 3.

5. Is it more likely that there will be a captain from each grade as compared to the probability that both captains will be in the same grade? Explain.

A bag contains three equal-sized tiles labeled 3, 5, and 7. Lin will flip
a coin and randomly choose a tile. Use an organized list or a table to
show all possible outcomes. How many outcomes are possible?

Organized List

(Heads, 3) (Heads, 5) (Heads, 7)

(Tails, 3) (Tails, 5) (Tails, 7)

The list and table both describe all
6 possible outcomes.

		Tile Number		
		3	**5**	**7**
Coin	**H**	(H, 3)	(H, 5)	(H, 7)
	T	(T, 3)	(T, 5)	(T, 5)

A deli provides sandwich wraps for a school group on a field trip. Each
wrap contains one meat, either chicken or turkey, and one vegetable,
either spinach or tomatoes. What outcomes are possible if a student
randomly selects a sandwich wrap?

1. What outcomes are possible for the meat in a randomly selected
   wrap? For the vegetable?

2. Complete the organized list below to describe the sample space.

   (_____, Spinach)   (_____, _____)

   (Turkey, Spinach)   (Turkey, _____)

3. How many outcomes are possible?

On the Back!

4. A bag contains three equal-sized tiles labeled 2, 4, and 6. A different
   bag contains three equal-sized tiles labeled with the letters Q, R and
   S. Inez will randomly choose one tile from each bag. What are all the
   possible outcomes?

Use terms from the list below to complete the sentences.

compound event	sample space	outcomes

A spinner is divided into three equal-sized sections: blue, green, and yellow.
If the pointer of the spinner is spun and a standard fair coin is flipped, what are
the possible outcomes?

1. A tree diagram can be used to describe all possible

   _____ .

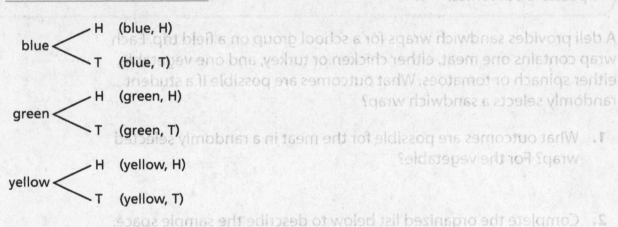

2. You can also list each possible outcome in an organized list to

   represent the _____ of this event.

   {(blue, H), (blue, T), (green, H), (green, T), (yellow, H), (yellow, T)}

3. A table can also be used to describe all possible outcomes of a

   _____ .

	Heads (H)	Tails (T)
Blue (B)	(B, H)	(B, T)
Green (G)	(G, H)	(G, T)
Yellow (Y)	(Y, H)	(Y, T)

Name _____

Read the problem below. Then answer the questions to understand the problem.

Megan will spin the pointer of the spinner shown and roll a number cube with sides numbered from 1 through 6. What are all the possible outcomes?

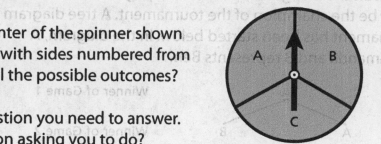 

1. Underline the question you need to answer. What is the question asking you to do?

2. A compound event consists of two or more events. Is this a compound event? If so, what are the different events?

3. What are the possible outcomes for each simple event identified in Exercise 1?

4. A sample space shows all the possible outcomes of a compound event. What are three different strategies or methods that could be used to represent the sample space in this exercise?

5. How many outcomes are possible for this compound event? Explain.

Amanda and Ben are playing a table tennis tournament. Amanda
has already won the first game, and the first player to win
3 games will be the champion of the tournament. A tree diagram
for the tournament has been started below. In the diagram, A
represents Amanda and B represents Ben.

Winner of Game 1

Winner of Game 2

1. Draw and label the next row of the tree diagram above. Leave
   space for additional rows.

2. Are there any branches in the tree diagram that will not continue
   to the fourth row? Explain.

3. What is the greatest possible number of games in the match? How
   is this related to the number of rows needed to complete the tree
   diagram above?

4. Complete the tree diagram above. Explain how to determine
   whether a branch will continue to the next row.

5. After Amanda wins the first game, how many different ways can
   the tournament unfold? Explain.

In a certain board game, a player who lands on the *Double Spin* space earns two spins of the pointer shown. This player is awarded a free turn if the pointer lands in the red section both times. What is the probability that a player who lands on the *Double Spin* space will win a free turn?

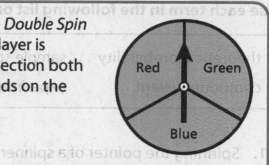

Make a table to describe the possible outcomes.

	Red (R)	**Green (G)**	**Blue (B)**
Red (R)	(R, R)	R, G	R, B
Green (G)	G, R	G, G	G, B
Blue (B)	B, R	B, G	B, B

- There are 9 possible outcomes.
- Each outcome is equally likely.
- The one favorable outcome is circled.

The probability that a player will win a free turn is $P(R, R) = \frac{1}{9}$.

To play a carnival game, a player tosses a coin into a large circular container. Equal-sized sections are painted different colors on the bottom of the container as shown. The player wins if the center of the coin lands in the green section and facing heads up. What is the probability that a player will win?

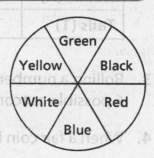

1. List all possible outcomes to describe where the the coin may land. Are the outcomes equally likely?

2. List all possible outcomes to describe the side of the coin that may be facing up when the coin lands in the container. Are the outcomes equally likely?

3. Describe all possible outcomes of the carnival game.

4. Find the probability that a player wins the carnival game.

On the Back!

5. Find the probability of winning the carnival game if a player wins when the center of the coin lands in the yellow section and facing tails up.

Name _____

Use each term in the following list once to complete the sentences below.

theoretical probability	sample space	outcomes
compound event	experimental probability	simple event

1. Spinning the pointer of a spinner twice and landing on blue both times is a(n) _____ .

2. The table below describes the _____ for flipping a coin and rolling a number cube.

	1	2	3	4	5	6
Heads (H)	H, 1	H, 2	H, 3	H, 4	H, 5	H, 6
Tails (T)	T, 1	T, 2	T, 3	T, 4	T, 5	T, 6

3. Rolling a number cube is a(n) _____ with 6 possible outcomes.

4. When a fair coin is flipped, there are two possible _____ .

5. The table below shows the results of rolling a number cube 100 times. According to the table, the _____ of rolling the number 3 is $\frac{19}{100}$.

Rolling a Number Cube						
	1	2	3	4	5	6
Number of Occurrences	16	13	19	13	21	18

6. A bag of 26 tiles contains one tile labeled with each letter of the alphabet. The _____ that the letter T is randomly selected from the bag is $\frac{1}{26}$.

Name _____

**Read the problem below. Then answer the questions
to understand the problem.**

Each month, students who volunteer as math tutors are entered into a
drawing for one of two gift cards to use at the school store. Arnie, Carol
Ed, Frank, and Liz volunteered this month and are all eligible candidates
for the drawing. What is the probability that Arnie will win one of the
two gift cards?

1. Underline the question you need to answer.

2. What is the meaning of the word *eligible* in this situation?

3. Describe a strategy that could be used to answer the question in
   this problem.

4. Describe all outcomes that are possible if Carol wins the first
   gift card.

5. What condition will be included in each favorable outcome in the
   context of the question asked?

Name _____

In this activity, you will explore probabilities of compound events.

1. What is the probability that a fair coin will land facing tails up when flipped?

2. Use a table, tree diagram, or organized list to find the probability that two fair coins flipped at the same time will both land facing tails up. Explain your answer.

3. A fair coin is flipped, a number cube is rolled, and the pointer of the fair spinner shown at right is spun. Use a tree diagram to describe the sample space. What is the probability that the coin lands facing heads up, the number 4 is rolled on the number cube, and the pointer of the spinner lands in section E?

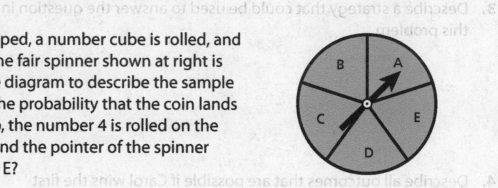

Tom is considering going on a road trip this weekend. There is a 75% chance of snow each day. He uses a spinner to simulate whether snow will fall each day. Based on Tom's results, what is the probability that it will snow on both Saturday and Sunday?

Trial 1	Result
Saturday	N
Sunday	S

Trial 2: S, S   Trial 3: S, S

Trial 4: S, S   Trial 5: N, N

Of 5 simulated trials, 3 predict snow on both days. Based on Tom's simulated results, the probability that it will snow both days is $\frac{3}{5}$.

Emma is successful on 80% of free throws she attempts this basketball season. She uses the spinner shown to simulate her next 4 attempts. The sections labeled 1 through 4 represent successful attempts, and the section labeled 5 represents missed attempts. Based on the simulated results shown below the spinner, what is the probability that Emma will successfully make exactly 2 of her next 4 attempted free throws?

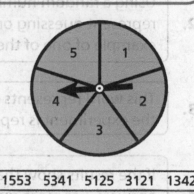

| 1553 | 5341 | 5125 | 3121 | 1342 |

1. Describe the results of the first simulated trial.

2. For how many of the 5 simulated trials do the data predict exactly 2 successful baskets?

3. Based on the simulated data, what is the probability that Emma successfully will make exactly 2 of her next 4 attempted free throws?

On the Back!

4. Emma conducts 5 additional trials and records the simulated data below. Based on the results of all 10 trials, what is the probability that Emma will successfully make at least 3 of her next 4 attempted free throws?

3321   5414   2422   2335   4224

A student randomly selects each answer of a multiple-choice quiz that has 5 questions. Each question has one correct answer out of 3 answer choices. To find the probability that the student will answer 3 or more questions correctly, a random number generator can be used to choose 5 random numbers between 1 and 3, where 1 represents a correct answer. Ten simulated trials of this experiment are conducted.

Match each description in Column A with the corresponding term in Column B.

Column A	Column B

1. This is the set of all possible answers to the 5 multiple-choice questions.

experimental probability

2. Using a random number generator to represent guessing on the quiz is an example of one of these.

trial

3. This word represents each of the 10 times the experiment is repeated.

sample space

4. If the results show that the student answers 3 or more questions correctly in 2 of 10 trials, then this is represented by $\frac{1}{5}$.

simulation

Name _____

**Read the problem below. Then answer the questions to
help understand the problem.**

In a board game tournament, Janelle and Rick will play 7 games. The
winner of 4 games will win the championship. Janelle and Rick have
played each other 10 times before, and each has won 5 games. What is
the probability that Janelle will win the tournament?

1. Underline the question in this exercise.

2. How could you develop a probability model for this situation?

3. Circle the numbers in the text. What information do the
    numbers provide?

4. How can a simulation be used to answer this question?

5. Describe a tool that can be used to simulate a single board game. Explain.

6. How many trials should be conducted? Describe the possible
    advantage of conducting more trials.

Joanna wants to choose 10 dates, at random, to conduct a survey of people at a park. She uses a computer program to generate 10 groups of 10 random numbers from 1–365 as shown below. Each number represents one of the 365 days in a standard year.

288	233	208	82	228	337	180	215	255	246
142	63	53	51	183	251	56	235	273	201
242	67	332	181	253	98	217	151	3	332
128	275	159	361	86	353	188	37	51	76
265	253	177	63	147	126	198	207	90	55
208	177	283	364	101	27	249	272	345	62
82	26	131	234	157	342	174	85	103	185
127	287	83	13	92	319	194	140	141	215
338	202	138	328	177	265	44	75	302	235
109	324	231	226	89	268	273	15	310	339

1. Each row of random numbers above can be used to represent the 10 dates. Using all of the rows, predict the following probabilities. Explain your reasoning.

a. Most of the events will occur in the second half of the year.

b. None of the events will occur in January.

c. At least two events will occur on the same day.

2. Some random number generators create a random list of the digits 0–9. How could this type of program be used to perform this simulation?

Name _____

Solve Problems Involving Geometry

Dear Family,

Your child is learning to solve a variety of problems involving angle measures, lengths, areas, and volumes of two- and three-dimensional figures, including triangles, quadrilaterals, circles, prisms, pyramids, and composite figures.

You can help develop your child's fluency with three-dimensional figures by doing the following activity.

Three Dimensions to Two

Materials: A three-dimensional object (such as a cracker box or salt container), paper, pencil, scissors, tape

Ask your child to cut paper that can be used to completely cover the three-dimensional object with no gaps or overlaps. Challenge him or her to make the paper covering in as few pieces as possible. Then have your child test his or her covering by placing it over the object, folding and taping as necessary.

Observe Your Child

Focus on Mathematical Practices

Look for and make use of structure.

Help your child become proficient with this Mathematical Practice. Have your child explain similarities and differences between coverings for two different three-dimensional objects (for example, the coverings of a rectangular prism and a cylinder).

Nombre _____

Resolver problemas de Geometría

Estimada familia:

Su hijo o hija está aprendiendo a resolver diversos problemas sobre medidas de ángulos, longitud, área y volumen de figuras bidimensionales y tridimensionales, como triángulos, cuadriláteros, círculos, prismas, pirámides y figuras compuestas.

Puede realizar la siguiente actividad para ayudar a su hijo o hija a adquirir fluidez con las figuras tridimensionales.

De una figura tridimensional a una figura bidimensional

Materiales: Un objeto tridimensional (por ejemplo, un envase de galletas saladas), papel, lápiz, tijeras, cinta adhesiva

Pida a su hijo o hija que recorte pedazos de papel que se puedan usar para recubrir completamente el objeto tridimensional, sin espacios vacíos y sin sobreposiciones. Anímelo a hacer la cubierta de papel con la menor cantidad de pedazos posible. Luego, pídale que ponga a prueba su cubierta colocándola sobre el objeto, doblando el papel y pegándolo con cinta adhesiva según sea necesario.

Observe a su hijo o hija

Enfoque en las Prácticas matemáticas
Buscar y utilizar la estructura.

Ayude a su hijo o hija a adquirir competencia en esta Práctica matemática. Pídale que explique las semejanzas y las diferencias entre cubiertas de dos objetos tridimensionales diferentes (por ejemplo, la cubierta de un prisma rectangular y la de un cilindro).

In the scale drawing shown, the room is 3 centimeters long. What is the actual length of the room?

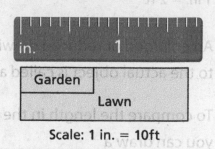

Room

Scale: 1 cm = 3 m

$\frac{3\text{ m}}{1\text{ cm}} = \frac{x\text{ m}}{3\text{ cm}}$ Use the scale $\frac{3\text{ m}}{1\text{ cm}}$ to write a proportion.

$3 \cdot \frac{3}{1} = 3 \cdot \frac{x}{3}$ Multiply both sides by 3.

$9 = x$ Simplify.

The actual length of the room is 9 meters.

The garden in the scale drawing is 0.75 inch long.

What is the actual length of the garden?

in.   1

Garden

Lawn

Scale: 1 in. = 10ft

1. Write the scale as a ratio: $\dfrac{\boxed{}\text{ ft}}{\boxed{}\text{ in.}}$

2. Write the ratio of the garden's actual length to its length in the drawing. Use the variable x to represent the unknown measurement.

3. Use the ratios determined in Exercises 1 and 2 to write a proportion.

4. By what number are both sides of the proportion multiplied to find x?

5. What is the actual length of the garden?

On the Back!

6. On a scale drawing, a park is 4.5 inches long. The scale is 0.5 inch = 10 feet. What is the actual length of the park?

Use terms from the list below to complete the sentences.

ratio	double number line	proportion
proportional relationship	scale drawing	

What is the actual length of the patio shown in the scale drawing?

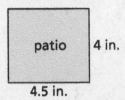

patio | 4 in.

4.5 in.

Scale: 1 in. = 2 ft

1. An enlarged or reduced drawing of an object that is proportional
   to the actual object is called a _____.

2. To compare the length in the drawing to the actual patio length,
   you can draw a _____ as shown below.

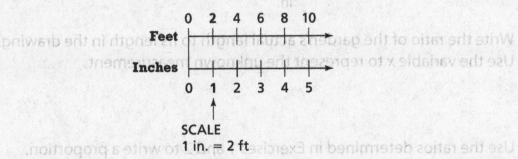

3. The length on the scale drawing and the actual length of the patio
   can be written as a _____ of 1:2.

4. To use the scale drawing to find the actual patio length you
   can write a _____.

   For example: $\dfrac{\text{drawing}}{\text{actual}} = \dfrac{1}{2} = \dfrac{4.5}{x}$

5. Because the measures of the scale drawing and the
   actual patio form a proportion, they represent a
   _____.

Name _____

What is the area, in square yards, of the playground represented
by the scale drawing?

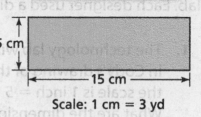

5 cm

|← 15 cm →|

Scale: 1 cm = 3 yd

1. Does the problem ask you to find the area of the
   playground in the scale drawing or the actual area of
   the playground?

2. What kind of relationship exists between the actual playground
   and the playground in the scale drawing?

3. Draw a circle around the scale in the drawing. Explain the meaning
   of the scale in your own words.

4. Let w represent the actual width of the playground. Circle a
   proportion you can use to find w.

   $\frac{1}{3} = \frac{w}{5}$ $\frac{3}{1} = \frac{w}{5}$ $\frac{3}{5} = \frac{w}{15}$ $\frac{5}{15} = \frac{w}{3}$

5. What unit will be used to express the actual area of the
   playground?

Several designers created scale drawings of a new technology
lab. Each designer used a different scale.

1. The technology lab will be a rectangular room with an area of 600 square feet.
   In Cody's drawing of the lab, the scale is 1 inch = 2 feet. In Paola's drawing,
   the scale is 1 inch = 5 feet, and one side of the lab measures 5 inches.
   What are the dimensions of the lab in Cody's drawing? Explain.

2. In Lin's drawing, the scale is 5 inches = 8 feet, and the back wall of the lab measures
   15 inches. Five computer workstations will be equally spaced along the entire
   length of that wall. Each workstation measures 4 feet by 4 feet. How far apart are
   the workstations in Lin's drawing? Explain.

3. The rectangular base of a 3-D printer is 4.5 feet by 3 feet. In Nika's drawing, the base
   of the printer is 3 inches by 2 inches. If Nika enlarges her drawing to 3 times its size,
   what will be the scale of her enlarged drawing? Explain.

4. The actual length of a rectangular platform used for assembling robots is 6 feet. In
   Jamal's drawing, the platform measures 1.2 inches in length and 1 inch in width.
   What is the actual width of the platform? Write a proportion to justify your answer.

The floor of a closet is 4 feet long and 2 feet wide and has four right angles. Make a scale drawing of the floor using a scale of 1 cm = 1 ft.

Use a ruler to draw a horizontal line segment that measures 4 centimeters. This represents the 4-ft side. Then use the corner of the ruler to draw a right angle.

Right angle

Use the ruler to extend the vertical side of the right angle to a length of 2 centimeters. This represents the 2-ft side. Repeat the process to complete the drawing.

4 cm

2 cm

The scale drawing shows that the floor is in the shape of a rectangle.

Yolanda cuts fabric into geometric shapes to make quilt pieces. She plans to make a four-sided fabric piece that has a 1-inch side that is adjacent to a 3-inch side, with the included angle between these two sides measuring 120°. She wants opposite sides of the shape to have the same length. Draw the quadrilateral that represents Yolanda's fabric piece.

1. Use a ruler to draw a side that measures 3 inches.

2. The side you drew in Exercise 1 will be one side of a 120° angle. Use a protractor to draw the other side of the angle and extend the line segment to measure exactly 1 inch.

3. Use a protractor to draw an angle that measures 60°. One side of the angle should be the side you drew in Exercise 2. Extend the new side to measure 3 inches in length, and then use a ruler to draw the last side of the quadrilateral. What is the length, in inches, of the last side?

4. Use a protractor to find the measure of the obtuse angle adjacent to the last side of the quadrilateral.

On the Back!

5. Yolanda also needs a fabric piece that is a square in which each side measures 4 inches. Make a drawing of this fabric piece.

Name _____

Complete the vocabulary chart.

Term	Definition	Drawing of Figure
quadrilateral	A quadrilateral is a figure with four sides.	
rectangle	A rectangle is a quadrilateral with exactly four right angles.	
square		
trapezoid		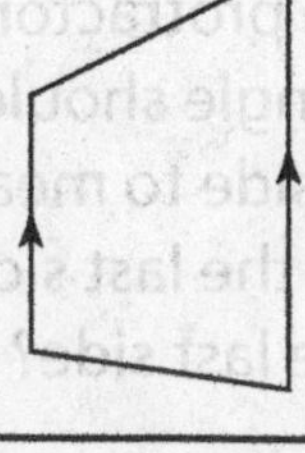
parallelogram		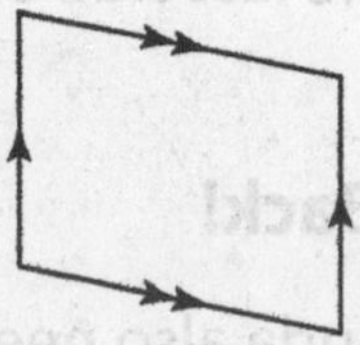

V 10-2

7

A restaurant has square tables that seat one person at each side. The restaurant staff must arrange several of these tables into one large rectangular table that seats 14 people. Make a sketch to show how many tables are needed.

1. Describe a correct answer to this problem.

2. Will you need to use tools, such as a ruler or a protractor, to solve this problem? Why or why not?

3. Make a sketch that shows two square tables arranged to form one rectangular table. How many people can sit at this new table?

4. How many ways can four square tables be arranged to form one rectangular table? Explain.

5. Is it possible that there is more than one correct answer to this problem? Explain.

Susana designs costume jewelry using plastic "gems" that are shaped like different quadrilaterals. Sometimes she arranges two or more gems to create different shapes.

1. Susana has four identical square gems. She wants to arrange them to form a larger quadrilateral with four right angles and two pairs of parallel sides. Susana's assistant says that the quadrilateral must be a square, as shown. Do you agree? If so, explain your reasoning. If not, draw a quadrilateral to support your answer.

2. Two gems are identical with angles measuring 90°, 90°, 45°, and 135°. Each gem has exactly one pair of parallel sides. Susana wants to use the gems to create a larger quadrilateral with two pairs of parallel sides and four right angles. Draw a possible arrangement. What are the names of the figures in your drawing?

3. A gem has two sides that each measure $\frac{1}{2}$ inch in length, two sides that each measure $\frac{3}{4}$ inch in length, and no right angles. What geometric names could be used to describe the gem?

4. Susana arranged three identical gems to form a regular hexagon. Draw lines on the hexagon to show three identical quadrilaterals. What geometric names could be used to describe the three identical gems?

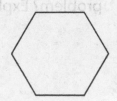

How many triangles can be drawn with a side length of 4 inches included between angles that measure 30° and 60°?

Draw a 4-inch line segment and rays that form the 30° and 60° angles.

There is only one way to draw the other two sides. Extend the rays until they intersect.

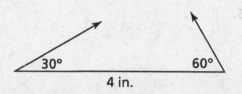

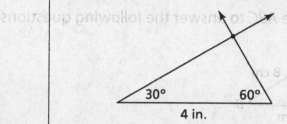

Only one triangle can be drawn given these conditions.

How many triangles that have sides measuring 4 centimeters and 5 centimeters in length, with an included angle measuring 55°, can be drawn?

1. Use a ruler and protractor to draw a 55° angle.

2. As necessary, extend or shorten one side of the angle to a length of 4 centimeters.

3. As necessary, extend or shorten the other side of the angle to a length of 5 centimeters.

4. Complete the triangle by drawing the third side. How many unique segments can be drawn to form the third side?

5. How many triangles that have sides measuring 4 centimeters and 5 centimeters in length with an included angle measuring 55° can be drawn?

On the Back!

6. How many triangles with angles measuring 45° and 55° with an included side measuring 3 inches in length can be drawn?

Use terms from the list below to complete the sentences.

included angle	greater than	unique triangle
triangle	nonincluded angle	line segment

Use triangle *ABC* to answer the following questions.

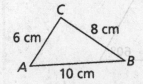

C
8 cm
6 cm
A
10 cm
B

1. The triangle symbol in △*ABC* is a quick way to write

   _____ *ABC*.

2. Side *AC*, which is between Point *A* and Point *C*, can also be called

   _____ *AC*.

3. The sum of the lengths of the two shortest segments must be

   _____ the length of the longest segment

   to form any triangle.

4. Angle *B* is a(n) _____ between sides *AB*

   and *BC*.

5. Triangle *ABC* is called a(n) _____ because

   there is only one triangle that can be drawn with these exact

   dimensions.

6. Because Angle *A* is not between sides *AB* and *BC*, it is a(n)

   _____ .

Name _____

Review the Key Concept from the lesson. Then answer the questions to help you understand how to read a Key Concept.

KEY CONCEPT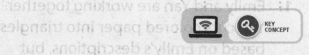

You can analyze given conditions of side lengths and angle measures to determine whether one unique triangle, more than one unique triangle, or no triangle can be drawn.

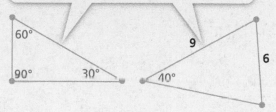

There is more than one possible triangle given these cases: all three angles, or two sides and a nonincluded angle.

60° 90° 30° 9 40° 6

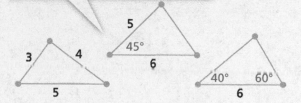

There is one unique triangle given these cases: all three sides, two sides and an included angle, or two angles and an included side.

3 4 5 5 45° 6 40° 60° 6

1. In the sentence at the top of the Key Concept box, underline the three possibilities when given side lengths and angle measures of triangles.

2. How are the diagrams related to the text underlined in Exercise 1?

3. Circle each case in both callout boxes. Then draw lines connecting each case to the matching triangle diagram.

4. Can diagrams with other side lengths and angle measures be used? Explain.

Students in an art class are creating mosaics using a variety of geometric shapes, including triangles.

1. Emily and Yan are working together. Yan cuts colored paper into triangles based on Emily's descriptions, but none of Yan's triangles match what Emily wants. Emily claims that Yan must not have followed her instructions correctly. Do you agree with Emily? Explain.

Triangle Color	Emily's Description
Blue	Angles: 50°, 60°, and 80°
Red	Side lengths: 3 inches, 5 inches Nonincluded angle: 120°
Green	Right triangle with two 45° angles

2. Candace draws a triangle with side lengths of 6 inches, 7 inches, and 9 inches. She plans to draw a second triangle that shares the 9-inch side with the first triangle. At each end of this shared side, the second triangle will have an angle measuring 60°. Describe the possible triangles that Candace can draw. Explain.

3. Juan constructs a triangle with sides that measure 5 inches and 3 inches in length with an obtuse angle included between these sides and a 30° angle that is not included between these sides. He claims that he can cut away part of the triangle and still have a triangle with sides that measure 5 inches and 3 inches in length and a 30° angle that is not included between these sides. Is Juan correct? Explain. Use a drawing to support your answer.

In the diagram, which angles are adjacent to $\angle VWX$?
What is the value of x?

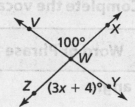

Adjacent angles are angles that share a ray.
$\angle VWZ$ and $\angle XWY$ are adjacent to $\angle VWX$.

$\angle YWZ$ and $\angle VWX$ are vertical angles, so they have equal measures.

$m\angle YWZ = m\angle VWX$	Write an equation.
$3x + 4 = 100$	Substitute values from the diagram.
$3x + 4 - 4 = 100 - 4$	Subtract 4 from both sides.
$3x = 96$	Simplify.
$\dfrac{3x}{3} = \dfrac{96}{3}$	Divide both sides by 3.
$x = 32$	Simplify.

In the diagram, what type of angles are $\angle ABE$ and $\angle DBC$:
adjacent angles or vertical angles? What is the value of x?

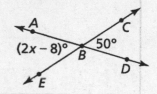

1. Do $\angle ABE$ and $\angle DBC$ share a ray?

2. Are $\angle ABE$ and $\angle DBC$ opposite each other?

3. What type of angles are $\angle ABE$ and $\angle DBC$: adjacent angles or vertical angles?

4. Write an equation that relates the measure of $\angle ABE$ to the measure of $\angle DBC$.

5. Solve the equation from Exercise 4. What is the value of x?

On the Back!

6. $\angle QRS$ and $\angle TRS$ are adjacent angles that are complementary. The measure of $\angle QRS$ is 78°. What is the measure of $\angle TRS$?

Complete the vocabulary chart.

Word or Phrase	Definition	Example
angle	An angle is a figure formed by two rays with a common endpoint.	
adjacent angles	Adjacent angles are angles that share a ray.	
vertical angles		∠1 and ∠3 are vertical angles. ∠2 and ∠4 are vertical angles.
complementary angles	Two complementary angles have measures that add to 90°.	
supplementary angles		45° 135°

Name _____

Three hiking paths intersect as shown in the diagram. Find the measure of ∠WEB.

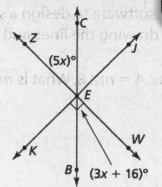

1. In the diagram, highlight ∠WEB.

2. What information about angle measures is given in the diagram?

3. Which angles in the diagram are complementary? Explain.

4. Circle the equation that can be solved to find the value of x in the diagram.

   $3x + 16 = 90$ $5x = 3x + 16$ $3x + 16 + 5x = 180$ $5x = 90$

5. When you find the value of x, have you solved the problem? Explain.

Name _____

Carla is using geometry software to design a stained-glass window. She begins by drawing the lines and angles shown.

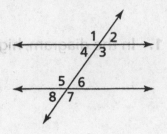

1. $m\angle 2 = 55°$ and $m\angle 4 = m\angle 8$. What is $m\angle 6$? Explain.

2. Carla's assistant, Joe, says that if $m\angle 1 = m\angle 5$, then $m\angle 3 = m\angle 7$. Is Joe correct? Justify your answer.

3. Carla adjusts the diagram so that $m\angle 5 = 2 \cdot m\angle 6$. Later, Joe adjusts the diagram again so that $m\angle 5 = 3 \cdot m\angle 6$. What is the change in $m\angle 6$ from Carla's adjustment to Joe's adjustment? Explain.

4. If Carla adjusts the diagram so that $\angle 1$ and $\angle 3$ are supplementary, what is $m\angle 2$? Explain.

5. Is it possible for Carla to adjust the diagram so that $\angle 2$ and $\angle 4$ are complementary? Explain.

Marsha made the ceramic plate shown. What is the
circumference of the plate? Use 3.14 for π.

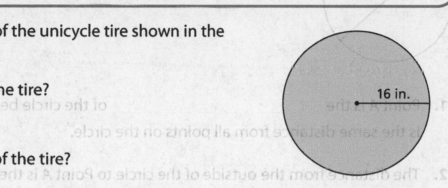

9.5 in.

$C = \pi d$	Formula for circumference
$C = \pi(9.5)$	The diameter is 9.5 inches.
$C \approx (3.14)(9.5)$	Use 3.14 for π.
$= 29.83$	Multiply.

The circumference of the plate is about 29.83 inches.

What is the circumference of the unicycle tire shown in the
diagram? Use 3.14 for π.

1. What is the radius of the tire?

16 in.

2. What is the diameter of the tire?

3. Fill in the boxes.

$C = \pi d$

$= \pi\left(\boxed{} \right)$

$\approx \left(\boxed{} \right)\left(\boxed{} \right)$

$= \left(\boxed{} \right)$

4. What is the circumference of the unicycle tire?

On the Back!

5. The circular top of a clay pot has a diameter of 14 centimeters.
   What is the circumference of the pot's circular top? Use 3.14 for π.

Name _____

Use terms from the list below to complete the sentences and the chart.

ratio	circumference	3.14
diameter	center	radius
$\frac{22}{7}$	π	

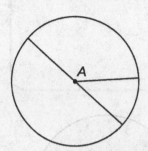

1. Point *A* is the _____ of the circle because it

   is the same distance from all points on the circle.

2. The distance from the outside of the circle to Point *A* is the

   _____.

3. The distance across the circle through Point *A* is the

   _____.

4. The distance around the circle is the _____.

All About Pi	
Symbol	
Definition	π represents the _____ of the circumference of a circle to its diameter.
Decimal Approximation of Pi	
Fractional Approximation of Pi	

Name_____

The large gear turns three times per second. It causes the small
gear to turn. How many turns does the small gear make in
one second?

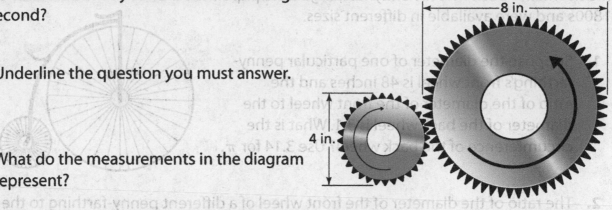

1. Underline the question you must answer.

2. What do the measurements in the diagram
   represent?

3. How is the number of turns made by the small gear related to the
   number of turns made by the large gear?

4. Circle the information that describes how many turns the large
   gear makes in one second. Will the small gear make more or fewer
   turns per second? How do you know?

5. How is this problem related to circumference? Once you find the
   circumference of the small gear, will you have solved the problem?
   Explain.

Name _____

A penny-farthing is a bicycle with a very large front wheel and a much smaller back wheel. Penny-farthings were popular in the 1800s and were available in different sizes.

1. Suppose the diameter of one particular penny-farthing's front wheel is 48 inches and the ratio of the diameter of the front wheel to the diameter of the back wheel is 3:1. What is the circumference of the back wheel? Use 3.14 for π.

2. The ratio of the diameter of the front wheel of a different penny-farthing to the diameter of the back wheel is 13:4. What is the ratio of the circumference of the front wheel to the circumference of the back wheel? Explain.

3. If the front wheel of another penny-farthing has a diameter of 56 inches and the back wheel has a diameter of 14 inches, how many turns, rounded to the nearest whole number, does the back wheel make when the penny-farthing travels 100 yards? Use 3.14 for π.

4. The back wheel of a different penny-farthing has a diameter of 15 inches. The front wheel makes 3 full turns for every 10 full turns of the back wheel. How far does the penny-farthing travel, to the nearest inch, for each full turn of the front wheel? Explain.

5. Another penny-farthing travels 52π inches with one full turn of the front wheel. What is the diameter of the front wheel? Explain.

A circular field in a park will be planted with sod.
Sod costs $3 per square yard.

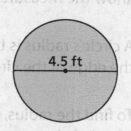

22 yd

The diameter is 22 yards, so the radius
is 22 ÷ 2 = 11 yards. Find the area.

$A = \pi r^2$	Formula for area of a circle
$\approx (3.14)(11)^2$	Substitute 3.14 for π and 11 for r.
$= 3.14(121)$	Simplify the power.
$= 379.94$	Multiply.

The area is about 380 square yards.

Find the cost: 3 × 380 = 1,140. The sod will cost $1,140.

Luke uses rug hooking to make a new rug. He estimates that
the cost of the yarn will be $5 per square foot. How much will
he spend on yarn?

4.5 ft

1. How do you find the radius of the rug? What is the radius
   of the rug in feet?

2. Fill in the boxes to find the area of the rug in square feet. Round
   the final area to the nearest tenth.

   $A = \pi r^2$

   $= \pi \left(\boxed{} \right)^2$

   $\approx \left(\boxed{} \right) \left(\boxed{} \right)$

   $\approx \left(\boxed{} \right)$ square feet

3. How do you find the cost of the wool for the new rug?

4. Find the cost of the wool.

On the Back!

5. Malik has a mirror in the shape of a circle. The mirror's diameter is
   76 centimeters. What is the area of the mirror? Use 3.14 for π.

Match each sentence with the word or phrase that best completes it.

1. The number of square units that cover a circle is the…

center of the circle.

2. To find the area of a circle, you need to know the measure of its…

A = πr².

3. A circle's radius is the distance from the edge of the circle to the…

2.

4. To find the radius, divide the diameter of a circle by…

3.14 or $\frac{22}{7}$.

5. To find the area of a circle, use the formula…

radius.

6. Common approximations for π are…

area of a circle.

Name _____

Micah is buying gravel for a rock garden that will be edged by a circular metal border. She will use 110 feet of metal edging for the border. What is the area of the garden? Use 3.14 for π.

1. Underline the question you need to answer. What will be the units of the answer?

2. What formula can be used to find the area of a circle?

3. What is the unknown measure you must find before you can calculate the area of the garden?

4. What part of a circle is described by the measurement given in the problem?

5. The equation $C = 2\pi r$ is used to determine the circumference of a circle with radius r. Describe how you can substitute and simplify this equation to help solve the problem.

Name _____

Neil is creating a computer game in which bubbles represented
by circles collide, merge, and separate in different ways.

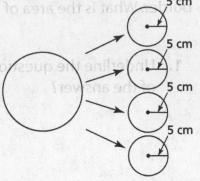

1. One large bubble separates into four small bubbles
so that the total area of the small bubbles is equal to
the area of the large bubble. Each small bubble has
a radius of 5 centimeters. What is the radius of the
large bubble?

2. Two small bubbles that each have a radius of 3
centimeters collide and merge into one large bubble. The area of
the large bubble is equal to the sum of the areas of the two small
bubbles. To the nearest centimeter, what is the radius of the large
bubble?
Use 3.14 for π.

3. Which is greater: the area of a bubble whose radius is 7 centimeters
or the total area of seven bubbles, each of which has a radius of
1 centimeter? Explain.

4. A bubble with a radius of 8 centimeters separates into small
bubbles, each of which has a radius of 2 centimeters. The area
of the large bubble is equal to the sum of the areas of the small
bubbles. How many small bubbles are there?

5. A bubble may be enclosed in a square whose side
length is equal to the bubble's diameter. Four bubbles
in squares collide and merge into one large bubble in
a square. The area of the large bubble is equal to the
sum of the areas of the small bubbles. How is the side
length of the large square related to the side length of
one small square?

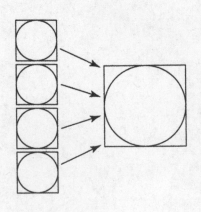

A cross section is the two-dimensional shape exposed when a three-dimensional shape is sliced. The shape and dimensions of a cross section are the same as the faces that are parallel to the slice.

Cam slices vertically through the rectangular block of cheese shown.

The cross section is the same shape as the left and right faces of the block because the cross section is parallel to the left and right faces.

The cross section is a square with sides that measure 4 inches in length.

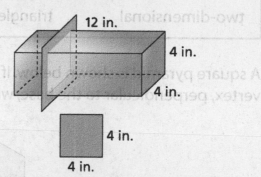

An artist will slice the rectangular block of red clay shown at right to make two layers. The artist will put a dividing layer of blue clay between the two layers as shown at right. Describe the shape and the dimensions, in centimeters, of the cross section.

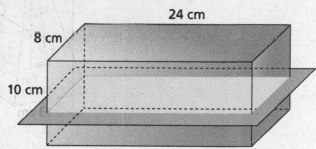

1. In what direction, horizontal or vertical, does the artist slice the block to create the cross section?

2. Which two faces of the rectangular block are parallel to the cross section?

3. What is the shape of the cross section?

4. What are the dimensions of the cross section?

On the Back!

5. The artist slices vertically through the original block of red clay shown above to expose a cross section parallel to the front and rear faces. Describe the shape and dimensions, in centimeters, of the cross section.

Use terms from the list below to complete the sentences.

point	three-dimensional	square
two-dimensional	triangles	isosceles

A square pyramid is shown below. If the pyramid is sliced vertically through the vertex, perpendicular to the base, what would the cross section look like?

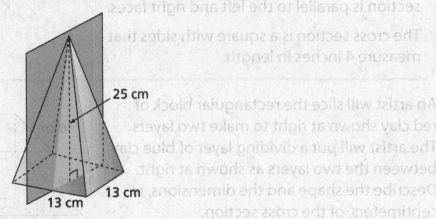

25 cm

13 cm   13 cm

13 cm

1. The pyramid is an example of a _____ figure.

2. The base of the pyramid is a _____.

3. The faces of the pyramid that are not its base are

   _____.

4. The vertex of the pyramid is the corner

   _____ that is not on the base of the

   pyramid.

5. A cross section is the _____ shape exposed when the pyramid is sliced.

6. The cross section is an _____ triangle because two of its sides are the same length.

Name _____

Riley will construct a plastic divider to separate food and
beverage items in his rectangular cooler shown at right.
What will be the shape and area, in square feet,
of the divider?

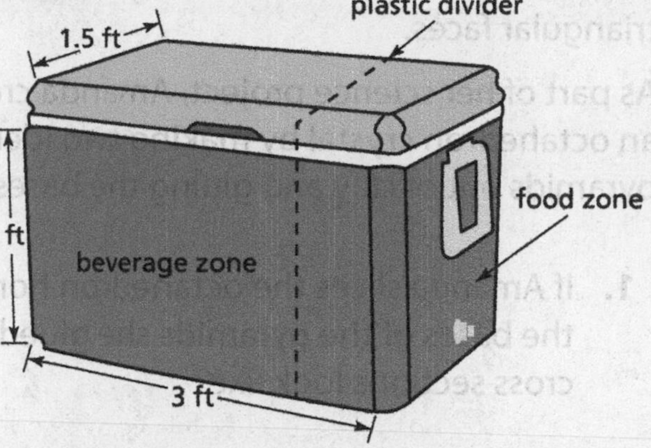

plastic divider

1.5 ft

food zone

2 ft

beverage zone

3 ft

1. Underline the question or questions
you need to answer.

2. Describe two methods you could use to answer the question
about what the divider should look like.

3. What type of three-dimensional object is the cooler?

4. What is the relationship between the divider and the cooler?

5. What information about the divider do you need in order to find its
area? Circle the parts of the diagram that show this information.

Name _____

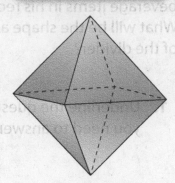

Natural crystals of fluorite often form in the shape of an octahedron, which is a three-dimensional figure with eight triangular faces.

As part of her science project, Amanda created a model of an octahedron crystal by making two identical rectangular pyramids out of clay and gluing the bases together, as shown.

1. If Amanda slices the octahedron horizontally, parallel to the bases of the pyramids she glued together, what will the cross sections look like?

2. How are the side lengths of the horizontal cross sections related to the side lengths of the pyramid bases that Amanda glued together?

3. A regular octahedron has eight faces that are identical equilateral triangles. Name the most specific geometric shape that describes the horizontal cross section.

4. Amanda slices her octahedron vertically, through the vertices of the pyramids and perpendicular to the bases she glued together. Name the most specific geometric shape that describes this cross section.

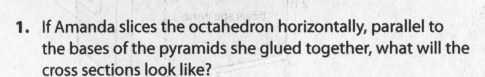

5. The vertical cross section created by Amanda in Exercise 4 has an area of 24 square inches. The distance from the vertex at the top of the octahedron to the vertex at the bottom is 8 inches, and the base of each pyramid is a square. What is the side length of the base of each pyramid?

Name _____

Murray is looking at a blueprint of the room shown below.
What is the area of the room?

Break the figure into composite parts. The dashed
line shown breaks the figure into a rectangle and
a trapezoid.

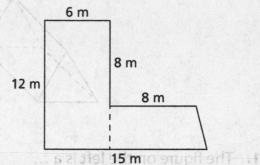

6 m

8 m

12 m

8 m

Find the area of the rectangle: 12 · 6 = 72. The
area of the rectangle is 72 square meters.

Find the dimensions, in meters, of the trapezoid.
Height: 12 − 8 = 4 meters; bottom base:
15 − 6 = 9 meters; top base: 8 meters

15 m

The area of the trapezoid is $\frac{9+8}{2} \times 4 = 34$ square meters.

The area of the room is 72 + 34 = 106 square meters.

The city is designing a park, shown in the drawing below. One section is
reserved for a parking lot. What is the area of the park?

1. What three shapes are created by the dashed lines?

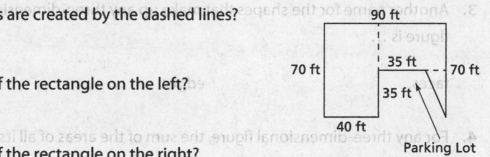

90 ft

70 ft

35 ft

70 ft

35 ft

40 ft

Parking Lot

2. What is the area of the rectangle on the left?

3. What is the area of the rectangle on the right?

4. What is the area of the triangle?

5. What is the total area of the park?

On the Back!

6. In the park shown above, what is the area of the parking lot?

Name _____

Circle the term or phrase that best completes each sentence.

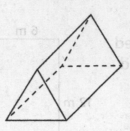 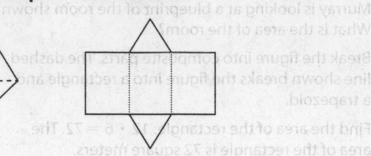

1. The figure on the left is a …

   triangular prism.   triangular pyramid.

2. The figure on the right is a …

   three-dimensional figure.   two-dimensional composite figure.

3. Another name for the shapes that make up any three-dimensional
   figure is …

   faces.   edges.

4. For any three-dimensional figure, the sum of the areas of all its
   faces is its …

   area.   surface area.

5. To find the area of any rectangle, multiply …

   length and width.   the square of the radius and π.

6. To find the area of any triangle, multiply …

   base times height.   one-half by the product of the base and height.

Nyla will use contact paper to cover the sides and bottom of her storage container that is shaped like a prism with two faces that are irregular pentagons. She will not cover the two rectangles that form the top of the container. How much contact paper will she need?

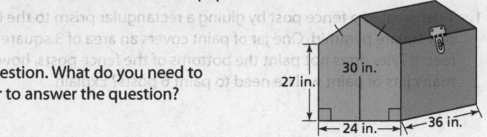

30 in.

27 in.

24 in.

36 in.

1. Underline the question. What do you need to calculate in order to answer the question?

2. Some of the faces that Nyla will cover cannot be seen. What do you know about these faces?

3. How could drawing a net help you solve this problem?

4. What shapes will appear in a net of this figure?

5. Are any shapes composed of smaller shapes? Explain.

6. What area formulas can you use to solve this problem?

M10·8

Members of the drama club are making props for an upcoming play. For some props, they construct prisms and pyramids of cardboard and then cover the surfaces to look like real-world objects.

1. Tyler created a fence post by gluing a rectangular prism to the base of a square pyramid. One jar of paint covers an area of 3 square feet. If Tyler does not paint the bottoms of the fence posts, how many jars of paint will he need to paint 6 posts? Explain.

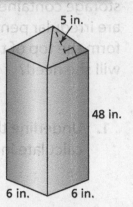
5 in.

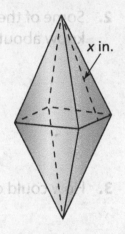
48 in.

6 in.   6 in.

2. To create a giant gemstone, Sara first made two identical square pyramids that each had a base area of 100 square inches. Then she glued the pyramids' bases together to form the gemstone. The surface area of the gemstone is 520 square inches. What is the value of x? Explain.

x in.

3. Tomi stacks four rectangular prisms to build a staircase. He plans to cover the tops, fronts, and sides of the stairs with brick-patterned paper. The rectangular prism at the top has a length of 11 inches, a width of 30 inches, and a height of 7 inches. How much paper, rounded to the nearest square foot, will Tomi need in order to cover the stairs? Explain.

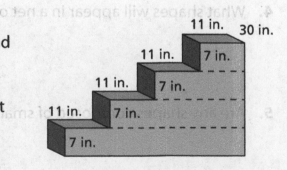
11 in. 30 in.
11 in.   7 in.
11 in.   7 in.
11 in.   7 in.
7 in.

Name _____

Raylene packs a specialty cake in the box shown. What is the
volume of the box?

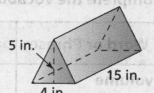

5 in.

15 in.

4 in.

Step 1 Find *B*, the area of the base.
The base is a triangle.

$B = \frac{1}{2}bh$ Formula for area of a triangle

$= \frac{1}{2}(4)(5)$ Substitute $b = 4$ and $h = 5$.

$= 10$ Simplify.

The area of the base is 10 square inches.

Step 2 Find the volume.

$V = Bh$ Formula for volume of a prism

$= 10(15)$ Substitute $B = 10$ and $h = 15$.

$= 150$ Simplify.

The volume of the box is 150 cubic inches.

Paula made a window box shaped like a prism. What is the volume of
the window box?

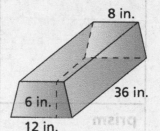

8 in.

36 in.

6 in.

12 in.

1. What shape is the base of the prism?

2. Complete the formula for the area of the shape identified in
   Exercise 1.

   $A = \dfrac{\square}{\square}(b_1 + b_2)\,\square$

3. Substitute given measurements into the formula to find the area of the base.

   $B = \dfrac{\square}{\square}\left(\boxed{} + \boxed{}\right)\boxed{}$

   $= \dfrac{\square}{\square}\left(\boxed{}\right)\left(\boxed{}\right)$

   $= \boxed{}$

4. What is the volume of the window box?

   $V = Bh$

   $= \boxed{}\left(\boxed{}\right)$

   $= \boxed{}$ cubic inches

On the Back!

5. A playground has a tunnel in the shape of a triangular
   prism. What is the volume of the tunnel?

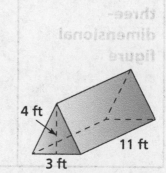

4 ft

11 ft

3 ft

Complete the vocabulary chart.

Word or Phrase	Definition	Example
volume		4 cm 3 cm 2 cm
cubic unit		1 unit 1 unit 1 unit
prism		
triangular prism	A triangular prism is a three-dimensional figure with two parallel bases that are triangles with equal dimensions.	
three-dimensional figure		Sphere Cone

Name _____

A planter is in the shape of a prism with bases that are
trapezoids. What is the volume of the planter?

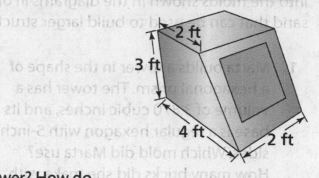

1. Underline the question in the exercise.

2. What units will be used to express the answer? How do
   you know?

3. On the diagram, sketch an outline of the trapezoid base of the
   prism. Circle the measures that give information about the base
   of the prism. What are the dimensions, in feet, of the base of
   the prism?

4. Circle the formula that you can use to find the area of the
   prism's base.

   $A = \frac{1}{2}bh$ $A = Bh$ $A = \frac{1}{2}(b_1 + b_2)h$

5. When you find the area of the prism's base, will you have
   completely solved the problem? Explain.

Name _____

Marta has entered a sand castle building contest. She packs sand into the molds shown in the diagrams in order to form "bricks" of sand that can be used to build larger structures.

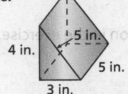
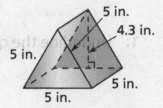
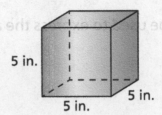
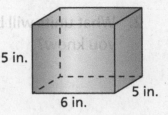

1. Marta builds a tower in the shape of a hexagonal prism. The tower has a volume of 3,870 cubic inches, and its base is a regular hexagon with 5-inch sides. Which mold did Marta use? How many bricks did she make with this mold? What is the height of the tower in feet?

2. A wall of sand is a rectangular prism 10 feet long and 5 inches wide. The wall contains 9,000 cubic inches of sand. What is the height of the wall in inches? How many more bricks made from the cube-shaped mold than bricks made from the rectangular prism-shaped mold are needed to construct this wall?

3. Describe how Marta could construct the two composite figures shown at right using the molds. Which figure requires more sand to build? How much more sand?

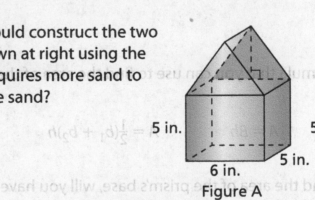
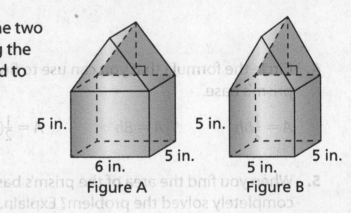

Figure A   Figure B

4. Marta has 1 cubic yard of sand to build a wall in the shape of a rectangular prism that is 20 inches tall and 5 inches wide. To the nearest foot, what will be the length of this wall? Explain.

Name _____

Congruence and Similarity

Dear Family,

Your child is studying transformations of figures, including translations, reflections, rotations, and dilations. He or she will apply transformations to determine whether figures are congruent or similar. Your child is also learning about angle relationships, such as the relationships among angles in a triangle and among angles created by different types of lines.

Here is an activity you can do with your child to help him or her practice transformations.

Transforming Shapes

Materials: Two identical shapes cut from paper, about 12 inches of string, coin or other small object

Step 1 Stack the paper shapes one on top of the other so that they align exactly.

Step 2 Choose a transformation: translation, reflection, or rotation. If you chose reflection, stretch the string in a straight line a few inches from the shapes. If you chose rotation, place the coin a few inches from the shapes and specify an angle of rotation, such as 90° or 180°.

Step 3 Have your child perform the selected transformation by picking up the top shape from the stack and translating, reflecting across the string, or rotating around the coin.

Step 4 Choose a different transformation and repeat.

Observe Your Child

Focus on Mathematical Practices
Attend to precision.

Help your child become proficient with this Mathematical Practice. Ask him or her to describe each transformation using the terms *preimage*, *image*, and *orientation*.

Nombre _____

Congruencia y semejanza

Estimada familia:

Su hijo o hija está estudiando transformaciones de figuras, como traslaciones, reflexiones, rotaciones y dilataciones. Aplicará transformaciones para determinar si las figuras son congruentes o semejantes. También está estudiando relaciones entre los ángulos; por ejemplo, las relaciones entre los ángulos de un triángulo y entre los ángulos que se crean a partir de diferentes tipos de rectas.

Esta es una actividad que pueden realizar juntos para que su hijo o hija practique las transformaciones.

Transformar figuras

Materiales: Dos figuras idénticas de papel recortado, aproximadamente 12 pulgadas de cuerda, una moneda u otro objeto pequeño

Paso 1 Apile las figuras de papel de modo que queden alineadas exactamente.

Paso 2 Escoja una transformación: traslación, reflexión o rotación. Si escoge la reflexión, estire la cuerda para formar una línea recta a algunas pulgadas de distancia de las figuras. Si escoge la rotación, coloque la moneda a algunas pulgadas de distancia de las figuras y especifique un ángulo de rotación, como 90° o 180°.

Paso 3 Pida a su hijo o hija que tome la figura de arriba de la pila para realizar la transformación escogida: una traslación, una reflexión al otro lado de la cuerda o una rotación alrededor de la moneda.

Paso 4 Escojan otra transformación y repitan la actividad.

Observe a su hijo o hija

Enfoque en las Prácticas matemáticas
Prestar atención a la precisión.

Ayude a su hijo o hija a adquirir competencia en esta Práctica matemática. Pídale que describa cada transformación usando los términos *preimagen*, *imagen* y *orientación*.

Graph △A′B′C′, the image of △ABC after a translation
3 units up and 2 units left.

Step 1

Translate each vertex of △ABC.

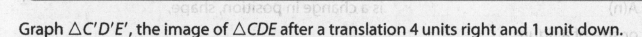

From point A, move 3 units up and 2 units left. Graph
and label point A′.

From point B, move 3 units up and 2 units left. Graph
and label point B′.

From point C, move 3 units up and 2 units left. Graph and
label point C′.

Step 2

Graph △A′B′C′ by connecting points A′, B′, and C′.

Graph △C′D′E′, the image of △CDE after a translation 4 units right and 1 unit down.

1. Start at point C. Move 4 units right and 1 unit down. Graph
   and label point C′.

2. From point D, move 4 units right and 1 unit down. Graph
   and label point D′.

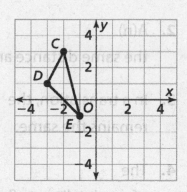

3. From point E, move 4 units right and 1 unit down. Graph
   and label point E′.

4. Graph △C′D′E′ by connecting points C′, D′, and E′.

On the Back!

△JKL has vertices J(2, 3), K(4, 5), and L(6, 1). Graph and label the
vertices of △JKL and △J′K′L′, its image after a translation 3 units
left and 5 units down.

Name _____

Use the list below to complete the sentences. Use each term once.
Use the figures on the coordinate plane as a reference.

corresponding points	corresponding sides	image
preimage	orientation	transformation	translation

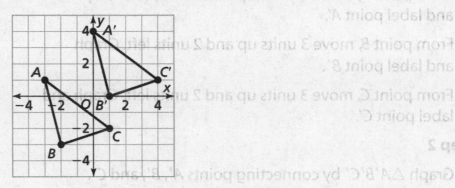

1. A(n) _____ is a change in position, shape,
or size of a figure.

2. A(n) _____ moves every point of a figure
the same distance and the same direction.

3. In a translation, the _____ of the figure
remains the same.

4. The _____ is the result of a transformation
of a point, line, or figure.

5. In the graph above, △*ABC* is the _____
of △*A'B'C'*.

6. After a translation, the lengths of _____
are equal.

7. After a translation, the distances between _____
have changed in the same way, vertically and horizontally.

Name _____

**Read the problem below. Then answer the questions to
identify the steps for solving the problem.**

△A'B'C' is a translation of △ABC. Describe the translation.

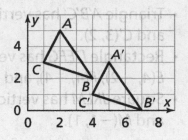

1. Which figure is the preimage, and which figure is the image?
   How do you know?

2. Why do you need to distinguish the image from the preimage to
   solve the problem?

3. To describe a translation, what information must you include?

4. What are the coordinates of points A and A'?

5. For a point in the preimage and its corresponding image,
   which coordinate changes in a horizontal translation? A vertical
   translation?

Name _____

Courtney is designing a video game in which geometric shapes move around the screen, using the graph shown.

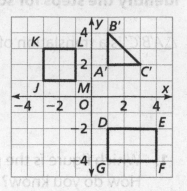

- Triangle $A'B'C'$ has vertices $A'(1, 2)$, $B'(1, 4)$, and $C'(3, 2)$.
- Rectangle $DEFG$ has vertices $D(1, -2)$, $E(4, -2)$, $F(4, -4)$, and $G(1, -4)$.
- Square $JKLM$ has vertices $J(-3, 1)$, $K(-3, 3)$, $L(-1, 3)$, and $M(-1, 1)$.

1. Triangle $A'B'C'$ is the image of triangle ABC after a translation 5 units up and 4 units right. Graph triangle ABC.

2. In triangle $A'B'C'$, $m\angle A'B'C' = 45°$. What is $m\angle ABC$ in triangle ABC? Explain.

3. Courtney translated rectangle $DEFG$ to create rectangle $D'E'F'G'$. What is the combined area, in square units, of rectangles $DEFG$ and $D'E'F'G'$? Explain.

4. Courtney translated square $JKLM$ to create square $J'K'L'M'$, so that it completely covers triangle $A'B'C'$. Describe a possible translation.

5. What is the perimeter, in units, of square $J'K'L'M'$? Explain.

Graph △A′B′C′, the image of △ABC after a reflection across the line x = −1.

Step 1 Reflect the vertices of △A′B′C′ across the line x = −1.

Each point in △A′B′C′ is the same distance from x = −1 as its corresponding point in △ABC, but on the opposite side.

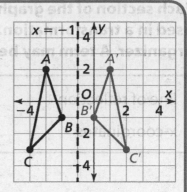

A is 2 units left of x = −1. Graph A′ 2 units right of x = −1.

B is 1 unit left of x = −1. Graph B′ 1 unit right of x = −1.

C is 3 units left of x = −1. Graph C′ 3 units right of x = −1.

Step 2 Graph △A′B′C′ by connecting A′, B′, and C′.

Graph △J′K′L′, the image of △JKL after a reflection across the line y = 1.

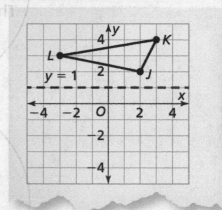

1. Point J is located how many units above y = 1? How can you use this information to plot point J′? Plot point J′.

2. Point K is located how many units above y = 1? Use this information to plot point K′.

3. Point L is located how many units above y = 1? Use this information to plot point L′.

4. Graph △J′K′L′ by connecting J′, K′, and L′.

On the Back!

5. △RST has vertices R(2, 1), S(−2, −1), and T(3, −2). Graph △RST and △R′S′T′, its image after a reflection across the line x = 2.

Each section of the graphic organizer contains a vocabulary term used in a transformation. Use the list below to complete the graphic organizer. A term may be used more than once.

line of reflection	reflection	orientation
x-coordinates	y-coordinates	

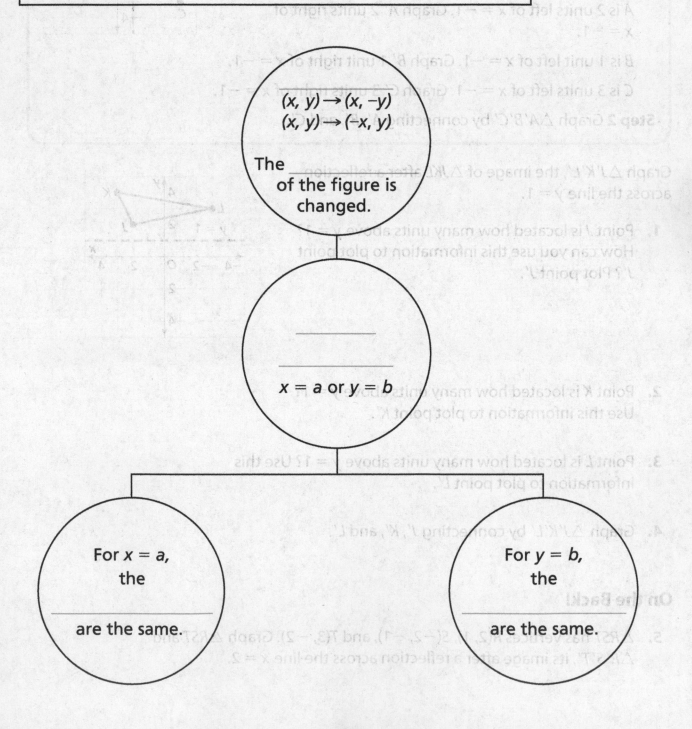

$$(x, y) \rightarrow (x, -y)$$
$$(x, y) \rightarrow (-x, y)$$

The _____
of the figure is
changed.

_____

$x = a$ or $y = b$

For $x = a$,
the

_____
are the same.

For $y = b$,
the

_____
are the same.

Name _____

Read the problem and connect it to the graph.

What is a rule that describes the reflection that maps
$\triangle EFG$ onto $\triangle E'F'G'$?

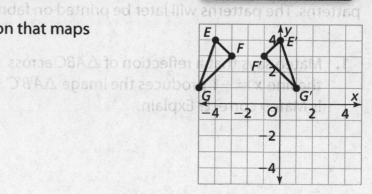

1. What does it mean that a reflection maps $\triangle EFG$ onto $\triangle E'F'G'$?

2. When describing a reflection, what information must you include?

3. On the graph, circle point *E*. Then circle the corresponding point in
$\triangle E'F'G'$. What is true about these two points?

4. How can you tell whether a line of reflection in the coordinate
plane is vertical or horizontal?

5. Draw the line of reflection on the graph.

Mateo is using a graphing program to create geometric
patterns. The patterns will later be printed on fabric.

1. Mateo says that a reflection of △ABC across
   the line $x = -1$ produces the image △A'B'C'.
   Is Mateo correct? Explain.

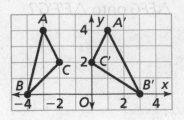

2. Mateo graphs quadrilateral EFGH and then reflects it across the
   line $y = 2$. How are the x-coordinates of corresponding points in
   the image and the preimage related?

3. Mateo graphs trapezoid JKLM, which has a height of 3 units and
   bases of 5 units and 7 units. Mateo then reflects JKLM across the
   y-axis to create J'K'L'M'. What is the area of J'K'L'M' in square units?

4. Mateo graphed parallelogram PQRS as shown. Then he
   graphed two reflections to create the design pictured.
   Describe the two reflections.

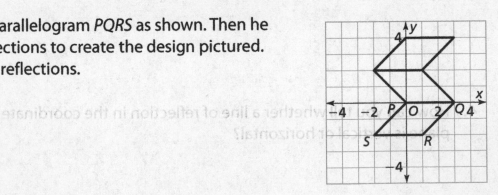

5. Mateo reflects WXYZ to create W'X'Y'Z'. The distance from W to the
   line of reflection is 4 units. What is the distance from W to W'?

Name _____

When a figure is transformed by a counterclockwise rotation about the origin, the x- and y-coordinates of its points change in predictable ways.

Counterclockwise Rotations About the Origin	
Angle of Rotation	**Transformation**
90°	$(x, y) \rightarrow (-y, x)$
180°	$(x, y) \rightarrow (-x, -y)$
270°	$(x, y) \rightarrow (y, -x)$

$\triangle A'B'C'$ is the image of $\triangle ABC$ after a 180° counterclockwise rotation about the origin.

Each point (x, y) is mapped to $(-x, -y)$:

$A(-1, 1) \rightarrow A'(1, -1)$

$B(-2, 3) \rightarrow B'(2, -3)$

$C(-4, 2) \rightarrow C'(4, -2)$

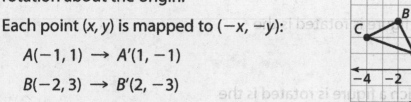

Describe the rotation that maps $\triangle QRS$ to $\triangle Q'R'S'$.

1. Write the coordinates of the vertices.

$Q\left(\boxed{}, \boxed{}\right) \rightarrow Q'\left(\boxed{}, \boxed{}\right)$

$R\left(\boxed{}, \boxed{}\right) \rightarrow R'\left(\boxed{}, \boxed{}\right)$

$S\left(\boxed{}, \boxed{}\right) \rightarrow S'\left(\boxed{}, \boxed{}\right)$

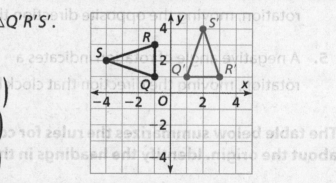

2. Circle the transformation of (x, y) that follows the same pattern as the change in coordinates from Q to Q', R to R', and S to S'.

$(x, y) \rightarrow (-y, x)$

$(x, y) \rightarrow (-x, -y)$

$(x, y) \rightarrow (y, -x)$

3. Refer to the table at the top of the page. Describe the rotation that maps $\triangle QRS$ to $\triangle Q'R'S'$.

On the Back!

4. $\triangle FGH$ has vertices $F(2, 1)$, $G(5, 1)$, and $H(5, 4)$. $\triangle F'G'H'$ has vertices $F'(-1, 2)$, $G'(-1, 5)$, and $H'(-4, 5)$. Describe the rotation that maps $\triangle FGH$ to $\triangle F'G'H'$.

Use each of these words to complete the definitions.

angle of rotation	center of rotation	clockwise
counterclockwise	rotation	

1. A transformation that turns a figure about a fixed point is a

   _____.

2. The number of degrees a figure is rotated is the

   _____.

3. The fixed point about which a figure is rotated is the

   _____.

4. A positive angle of rotation indicates a _____

   rotation, moving the opposite direction that clock hands move.

5. A negative angle of rotation indicates a _____

   rotation, moving the direction that clock hands move.

**The table below summarizes the rules for counterclockwise rotations
about the origin. Identify the headings in the top row of the table.**

6.

90°	$(x, y) \rightarrow (-y, x)$
180°	$(x, y) \rightarrow (-x, -y)$
270°	$(x, y) \rightarrow (y, -x)$

Name _____

Read the problem below. Then answer the questions to identify the steps for solving the problem.

Describe the rotation that maps △XYZ to △X'Y'Z'.

1. What is the problem asking you to find?

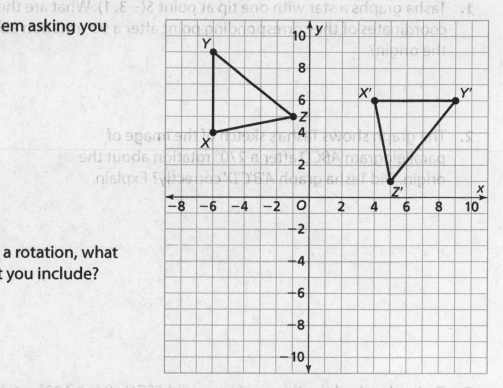

2. When describing a rotation, what information must you include?

3. On the graph, draw curved arrows between corresponding points on the triangles to show the rotation about the origin.

4. Write the coordinates of each point.

X(___ , ___)   X'(___ , ___)
Y(___ , ___)   Y'(___ , ___)
Z(___ , ___)   Z'(___ , ___)

5. How can you use the coordinates you identified in Exercise 4 to describe the rotation?

Tasha is creating animated objects for a website. She uses rotations in the coordinate plane to describe how the objects move.

1. Tasha graphs a star with one tip at point $S(-3, 1)$. What are the coordinates of the corresponding point after a 90° rotation about the origin?

2. The graph shows Tasha's sketch of the image of parallelogram ABCD after a 270° rotation about the origin. Did Tasha graph A'B'C'D' correctly? Explain.

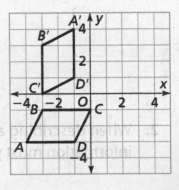

3. Tasha sketched the image of trapezoid EFGH after a 180° rotation about the origin. Then she sketched a second image of EFGH after a 540° rotation about the origin. How are the two rotations of EFGH related? Explain.

4. On the graph, label the vertices of the triangle that is an image of △PQR after a rotation. Describe the rotation.

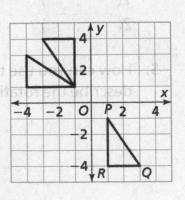

Reflect △ABC across the x-axis and then translate it
2 units left.

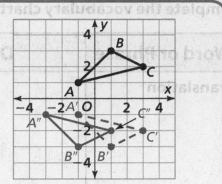

Step 1 Reflect △ABC across the x-axis.

$A(-1, 1) \rightarrow A'(-1, -1)$

$B(1, 3) \rightarrow B'(1, -3)$

$C(3, 2) \rightarrow C'(3, -2)$

Step 2 Translate △A'B'C' 2 units left.

$A'(-1, -1) \rightarrow A''(-3, -1)$

$B'(1, -3) \rightarrow B''(-1, 3)$

$C'(3, -2) \rightarrow C''(1, -2)$

Reflect △CDE across the y-axis and then translate it
3 units up.

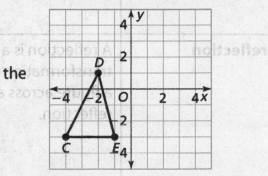

1. Reflect points C, D, and E across the y-axis. Label the
   resulting points C', D', and E'.

2. Draw △C'D'E'.

3. Translate points C', D', and E' 3 units up. Label the resulting points
   C'', D'', and E''.

4. Draw △C''D''E''.

On the Back!

5. △FGH has vertices F(−2, 1), G(−2, 4), and H(0, 2). Graph △FGH. Then reflect it
   across the x-axis and translate it 3 units down.

Complete the vocabulary chart.

Word or Phrase	Definition	Example
translation		Each point moves left 7 units. Figure *M'N'O'P'* is a translation of figure *MNOP*.
reflection	A reflection is a transformation that flips a figure across a line of reflection.	
rotation		*A'B'C'D'* is a rotation of *ABCD*. The origin is the center of rotation.

Name _____

Review the Key Concept from the lesson. Then answer the questions to help you understand how to read a Key Concept.

KEY CONCEPT

You can use a sequence of two or more transformations to map a preimage to its image.

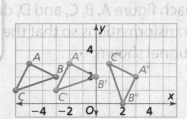

You can map $\triangle ABC$ onto $\triangle A''B''C''$ by a translation 3 units right followed by a 90° clockwise rotation about the origin.

1. How does the diagram in the Key Concept box show a sequence of two transformations?

2. Which triangle in the diagram is the preimage? Which is the final image? Explain.

3. Circle the text that describes the transformation from $\triangle ABC$ to $\triangle A'B'C'$. Then draw and label arrows on the diagram to show this transformation.

4. Underline the text that describes the transformation from $\triangle A'B'C'$ to $\triangle A''B''C''$. Then draw and label arrows on the diagram to show this transformation.

Name _____

Stephen is a playground designer. To lay out his designs, he uses a program that graphs and transforms figures in the coordinate plane.

1. Stephen wants to use four sections of tubing to create a tunnel for children to crawl through. For each figure A, B, C, and D, describe a sequence of transformations so that the images will form the tunnel shown.

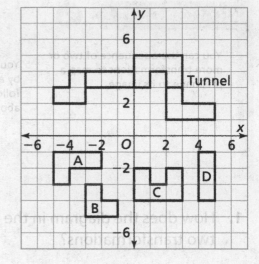

A:

B:

C:

D:

2. Stephen wants to build a sandbox in the shape of a pentagon by performing two transformations of △JKL so that the image △J″K″L″ forms a pentagon with rectangle EFGH. Describe a sequence of transformations that Stephen could use. Graph △J″K″L″.

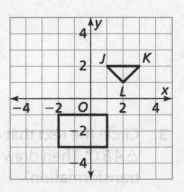

3. Can Stephen use a glide reflection to transform △JKL to the image △J″K″L″ that you found in Exercise 2? Explain.

Is △ABC congruent to △JKL? Explain.

Look for a sequence of transformations that maps △ABC onto △JKL.

Step 1 Reflect △ABC across the y-axis.

Step 2 Translate △A'B'C' 2 units up.

This sequence of transformations maps △ABC onto △JKL, so the triangles are congruent.

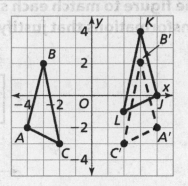

Is △DEF congruent to △LMN? Explain.

1. Reflect △DEF across the x-axis. Label the resulting triangle △D'E'F'.

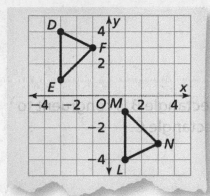

2. Is there a transformation that maps △D'E'F' onto △LMN? If so, describe the transformation. If not, explain why not.

3. Is △DEF congruent to △LMN? Explain.

On the Back!

4. △FGH has vertices F(1, 5), G(1, 2), and H(5, 2). △QRS has vertices Q(−1, 0), R(−1, −3), and S(−5, −3). Graph the two triangles on the same coordinate plane. Is △FGH congruent to △QRS? Explain.

**Use the figure to match each statement with the transformation
or transformations that justify it.**

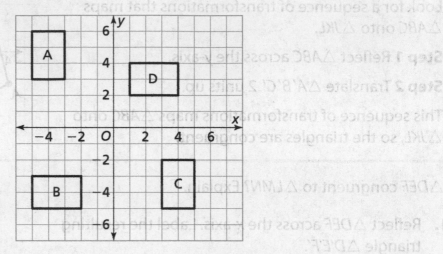

Rectangle B is congruent to
rectangle C.

A translation down 8 units, followed
by a reflection over the y-axis

Rectangle A is congruent to
rectangle C.

A 90° rotation counterclockwise
about the origin

Rectangle B is congruent to
rectangle D.

A 90° rotation clockwise about the
origin, followed by a translation down
1 unit and left 2 units

Rectangle A is congruent to
rectangle D.

A reflection over the x-axis, followed
by a translation down 1 unit and right
6 units

Name _____

Read the problem below. Then answer the questions to understand the problem.

Is $\triangle DEF \cong \triangle QRS$? Explain.

1. What does the symbol $\cong$ mean? What does it mean for two figures to have this relationship?

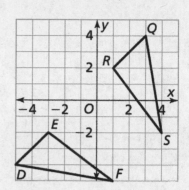

2. How can you determine whether $\triangle DEF \cong \triangle QRS$?

3. What information is contained in the graph?

4. Which point in $\triangle QRS$ corresponds to point D? To point F? To point E? Explain.

5. Do the triangles have the same orientation? How can you use this observation to help solve the problem?

Elin is competing in a puzzle contest. She is given the following puzzles.

1. Which puzzle piece will fit into the empty space? Explain.

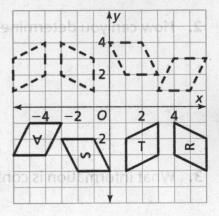

In this diagram of letter tiles and blank spaces, the tiles are clear. This is so the letters can be viewed whether the tile is face down or face up. Use the diagram for Exercises 2 and 3.

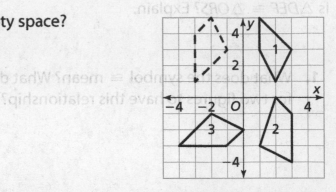

2. Elin needs to move the four letter tiles to the empty spaces to make a word so that each letter appears correctly in an upright position. What word can Elin make? Describe a sequence of transformations for each letter tile.

3. Is it possible for Elin to make a word starting with the letter 'A' tile such that it fits in an upright position in the first blank? Explain.

Draw the image of △ABC after a dilation with center (0, 0) and a scale factor of 2.

Step 1 Find the coordinates of the vertices of △ABC.

A(2, 1)   B(3, 3)   C(4, 2)

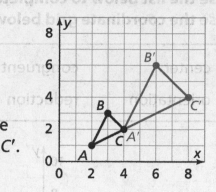

Step 2 Multiply the coordinates of A, B, and C by the scale factor, 2. Record the coordinates of the vertices of △A'B'C'.

$A(2, 1) \rightarrow A'(2 \cdot 2, 1 \cdot 2) = A'(4, 2)$

$B(3, 3) \rightarrow B'(3 \cdot 2, 3 \cdot 2) = B'(6, 6)$

$C(4, 2) \rightarrow C'(4 \cdot 2, 2 \cdot 2) = C'(8, 4)$

Step 3 Graph A', B', and C'. Connect the points to form △A'B'C'.

Draw the image of △CDE after a dilation with center (0, 0) and a scale factor of $\frac{1}{2}$.

1. Write the coordinates of the vertices of △CDE.

$C\left(\boxed{}, \boxed{}\right)$

$D\left(\boxed{}, \boxed{}\right)$

$E\left(\boxed{}, \boxed{}\right)$

2. Multiply the coordinates of C, D, and E by the scale factor to find the coordinates of C', D', and E'.

$C'\left(\boxed{} \cdot \frac{1}{2}, \boxed{} \cdot \frac{1}{2}\right) = C'\left(\boxed{}, \boxed{}\right)$

$D'\left(\boxed{} \cdot \frac{1}{2}, \boxed{} \cdot \frac{1}{2}\right) = D'\left(\boxed{}, \boxed{}\right)$

$E'\left(\boxed{} \cdot \frac{1}{2}, \boxed{} \cdot \frac{1}{2}\right) = E'\left(\boxed{}, \boxed{}\right)$

3. Graph C', D', and E'. Connect the points to form △C'D'E'.

On the Back!

4. △QRS has vertices Q(1, 3), R(2, 1), and S(3, 3). Graph △QRS and its image after a dilation with center (0, 0) and a scale factor of 3.

Name _____

Use the list below to complete the sentences. Use each term once.
Use the coordinate grid below as a reference.

center	congruent	dilation	enlargement
orientation	reduction	scale factor	

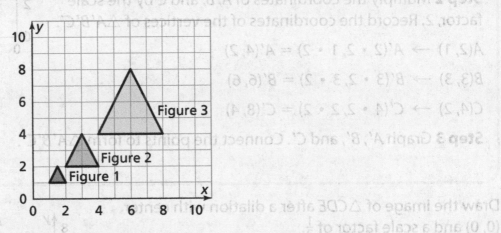

1. The result of a dilation that is larger than the original image is a(n)

   _____.

2. The result of a dilation that is smaller than the original image is a(n)

   _____.

3. The image that is the same shape, but not the same size as the

   preimage is a(n) _____.

4. In a dilation, the image and the preimage are not

   _____.

5. The ratio of a length in an image to the corresponding length in

   the preimage is the _____.

6. A dilation starts from a fixed _____ and

   multiplies distances from the center by a common scale factor.

7. A dilation results in an image with the same shape and

   _____ as the preimage.

Name _____

Read the problem below. Then answer the questions to identify the steps for solving the problem.

Rectangle *A'B'C'D'* is the image of rectangle *ABCD* after a dilation with center (0, 0). What is the scale factor of the dilation?

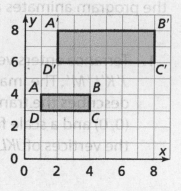

1. What does it mean that rectangle *A'B'C'D'* is the image of rectangle *ABCD* after a dilation?

2. What is the scale factor of a dilation?

3. Is this dilation an enlargement or a reduction? Explain.

4. What does your answer to Exercise 3 tell you about the scale factor?

5. How can you use the coordinates of a point in the preimage and the coordinates of the corresponding point in the image to find the scale factor?

Terrance is using an animated graphing program in his math class. He enters the vertices of a preimage and an image, and the program animates and describes the transformation.

1. Terrance enters vertices for trapezoid *JKLM* and its image *J'K'L'M'*. The image *J'K'L'M'* is shown. The program describes the transformation as a dilation with center $(0, 0)$ and a scale factor of $\frac{3}{2}$. What did Terrance enter as the vertices of *JKLM*?

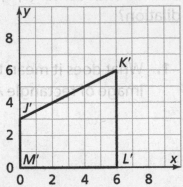

2. Terrance and his friend Connie both enter preimage coordinates $X(-1, 2)$, $Y(2, 1)$, and $Z(-1, -1)$ as well as image coordinates for *X'*, *Y'*, and *Z'*. The program describes a dilation with center $(0, 0)$ and the same scale factor for both students. Is it possible that Terrance and Connie entered different coordinates for *X'*, *Y'*, and *Z'*? Explain.

3. Terrance's teacher graphs quadrilateral *ABCD* on the board and asks the class to dilate *ABCD* using center $(0, 0)$ and a scale factor of 2. When Terrance checks his answer by entering the preimage and image coordinates into the program, the program describes the transformation as a dilation with center $(0, 0)$ and a scale factor of $\frac{1}{2}$. What error might Terrance have made?

4. Terrance enters preimage coordinates $E(5, 10)$, $F(0, 0)$, $G(5, 5)$ as well as the image coordinates for *E'*, *F'*, and *G'*. The program describes the transformation as a dilation with center $(0, 0)$. The scale factor the program gives is greater than 1 and less than 2. What are possible coordinates Terrance could have entered for *E'*, *F'*, and *G'*?

Graph △A"B"C", the image of △ABC by a dilation
with center (0, 0) and scale factor 0.5 and a
reflection across the y-axis.

Step 1 Graph the dilation.

Multiply the coordinates of A, B, and C by the scale
factor, 0.5, to find the coordinates of A', B', and C'.

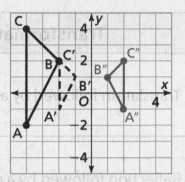

$A(-4, -2) \rightarrow A'(-2, -1)$

$B(-2, 2) \rightarrow B'(-1, 1)$

$C(-4, 4) \rightarrow C'(-2, 2)$

Step 2 Reflect △A'B'C' across the y-axis. Label
the resulting image △A"B"C".

Graph △D"E"F", the image of △DEF by a dilation with center
(0, 0) and scale factor 2 and a translation 3 units down.

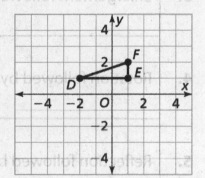

1. Multiply the coordinates of D, E, and F by
   the scale factor, 2, to find the coordinates of
   D', E', and F'.

   $D\left(\boxed{}, \boxed{}\right) \rightarrow D'\left(\boxed{}, \boxed{}\right)$

   $E\left(\boxed{}, \boxed{}\right) \rightarrow E'\left(\boxed{}, \boxed{}\right)$

   $F\left(\boxed{}, \boxed{}\right) \rightarrow F'\left(\boxed{}, \boxed{}\right)$

2. Graph △D'E'F'.

3. Translate points D', E', and F' 3 units down. Label the resulting
   points D", E", and F".

4. Graph △D"E"F".

On the Back!

5. △FGH has vertices F(1, 1), G(3, 1), and H(3, 2). Graph △F"G"H", the
   image of △FGH by a dilation with center (0, 0) and scale factor 3
   and a reflection across the x-axis.

**For each transformation described, write whether the image
is *congruent* or *similar* to the preimage.**

Transformation	Congruent or Similar?
1. Translation followed by a rotation	
2. Reflection followed by a dilation	
3. Enlargement followed by a rotation	
4. Rotation followed by a reflection	
5. Reflection followed by a rotation	
6. Translation followed by a reduction	
7. Dilation followed by a reflection	
8. Reduction followed by a reflection	

**Read the problem below. Then answer the questions to
understand the problem.**

Is △ABC ~ △DEF? Explain.

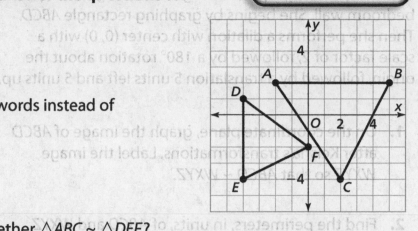

1. Rewrite the question using words instead of
   mathematical symbols.

2. How can you determine whether △ABC ~ △DEF?

3. Are the triangles the same size? How does this help you solve the problem?

4. Do the triangles have the same orientation? How does this help
   you solve the problem?

5. On the graph, circle point A and the point that corresponds to point A.
   How do you know that these two points are corresponding? Why is it
   important to identify corresponding points?

Keisha is planning a pattern of geometric figures to paint on her
bedroom wall. She begins by graphing rectangle *ABCD*.
Then she performs a dilation with center (0, 0) with a
scale factor of 2, followed by a 180° rotation about the
origin, followed by a translation 5 units left and 5 units up.

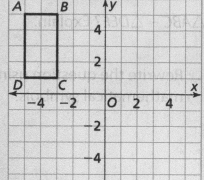

1. On the coordinate plane, graph the image of *ABCD*
   after Keisha's transformations. Label the image
   WXYZ so that *ABCD* ~ *WXYZ*.

2. Find the perimeters, in units, of *ABCD* and *WXYZ*.
   Describe the relationship between the perimeters in
   terms of the transformations.

3. Find the areas, in square units, of *ABCD* and *WXYZ*. Describe the
   relationship between the areas in terms of the transformations.

4. Keisha graphed parallelogram *QRST* and one side of
   parallelogram *JKLM*. She wants to graph points *J* and *K*
   so that *QRST* ~ *JKLM*. Find possible coordinates for
   J and *K* and describe a sequence of transformations
   that maps *QRST* to that version of *JKLM*.

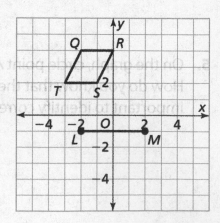

5. Is there more than one correct answer to Exercise 4? If so, give
   another possible answer. Explain.

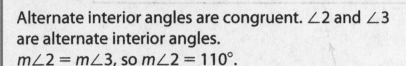

In the figure, $a \parallel b$ and $m\angle 1 = 110°$. What are the measures of $\angle 2$, $\angle 3$, and $\angle 4$?

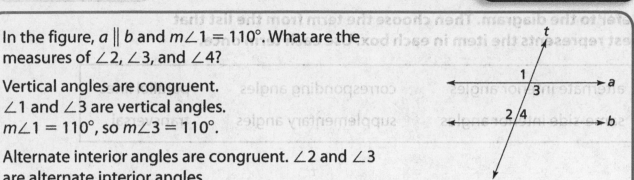

Vertical angles are congruent.
$\angle 1$ and $\angle 3$ are vertical angles.
$m\angle 1 = 110°$, so $m\angle 3 = 110°$.

Alternate interior angles are congruent. $\angle 2$ and $\angle 3$ are alternate interior angles.
$m\angle 2 = m\angle 3$, so $m\angle 2 = 110°$.

Same-side interior angles are supplementary.
$\angle 3$ and $\angle 4$ are same-side interior angles.

$m\angle 3 + m\angle 4 = 180°$
$110° + m\angle 4 = 180°$
$m\angle 4 = 70°$

In the figure, $c \parallel d$ and $m\angle 1 = 60°$. What are the measures of $\angle 2$, $\angle 3$, and $\angle 4$?

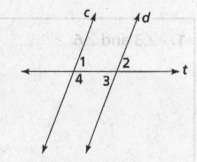

1. $\angle 1$ and which angle are corresponding angles? What is the measure of this angle?

2. $\angle 1$ and which angle are alternate interior angles? What is the measure of this angle?

3. Which two angles are same-side interior angles? What are the measures of these angles?

On the Back!

4. In the figure, $p \parallel q$ and $m\angle 1 = 125°$. What are the measures of $\angle 2$, $\angle 3$, and $\angle 4$?

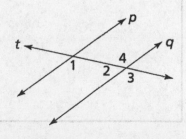

**Refer to the diagram. Then choose the term from the list that
best represents the item in each box. Use each term once.**

alternate interior angles	corresponding angles	parallel lines
same-side interior angles	supplementary angles	transversal

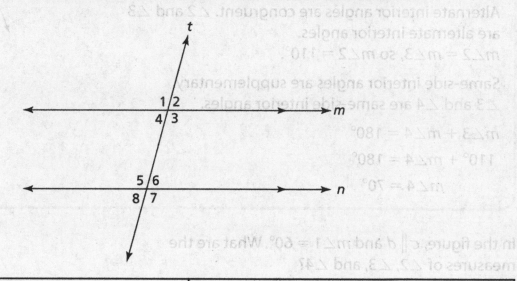

1. ∠3 and ∠6	**2.** ∠4 and ∠6
3. line *t*	**4.** lines *m* and *n*
5. ∠1 and ∠5	**6.** ∠4 + ∠5 = 180°

Name _____

Read the problem below. Then answer the questions to connect the problem to the diagram.

The measure of ∠4 is 75°. What is the measure of ∠7?

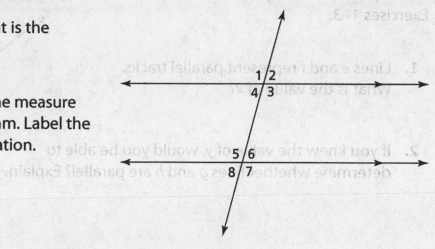

1. The problem text gives the measure of one angle in the diagram. Label the diagram with this information.

2. In the diagram, circle the angle whose measure you must find.

3. What information is given in the diagram that is not stated in the problem text?

4. Highlight the part or parts of the diagram that give the information you identified in Exercise 3.

5. What is the relationship between the measures of each type of angle listed below? Identify one pair of such angles from the diagram.

   Adjacent angles
   Relationship of angle measures: _____
   _____ Example: _____

   Vertical angles
   Relationship of angle measures: _____
   Example: _____

Before she sets up her model railroad tracks, Dana likes to
sketch possible arrangements. Use the sketch at right for
Exercises 1–3.

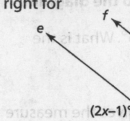

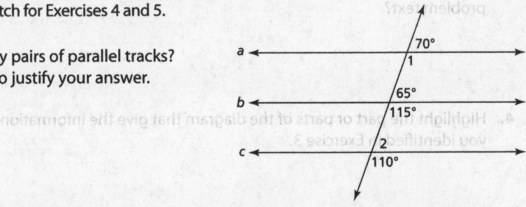

1. Lines *e* and *f* represent parallel tracks.
   What is the value of *x*?

2. If you knew the value of *y*, would you be able to
   determine whether lines *g* and *h* are parallel? Explain.

3. Is it possible to find the value of *z*? If so, find it. If not, explain why not.

In the sketch at right, lines *a*, *b*, and *c* represent railroad
tracks. Use the sketch for Exercises 4 and 5.

4. Are there any pairs of parallel tracks?
   Use angles to justify your answer.

5. Are there any pairs of tracks that are not parallel? Use angles to
   justify your answer.

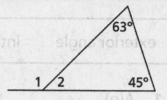

What are $m\angle 1$ and $m\angle 2$?

$\angle 1$ is an exterior angle of the triangle. The measure of an exterior angle of a triangle is equal to the sum of the measures of its remote interior angles.

$m\angle 1 = 63° + 45°$

$\qquad = 108°$

The sum of the measures of the interior angles of a triangle is 180°.

$m\angle 2 + 63° + 45° = 180°$

$\qquad m\angle 2 + 108° = 180°$

$\qquad\qquad m\angle 2 = 72°$

What are $m\angle 1$ and $m\angle 2$?

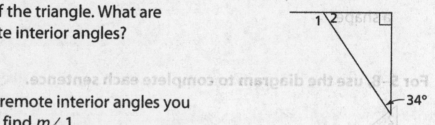

1. $\angle 1$ is an exterior angle of the triangle. What are the measures of its remote interior angles?

2. Add the measures of the remote interior angles you identified in Exercise 1 to find $m\angle 1$.

3. Complete the equation.

$m\angle 1 + m\angle 2 = \boxed{}$

4. Use your answer to Exercise 2 and the equation in Exercise 3 to find $m\angle 2$.

$\boxed{} + m\angle 2 = \boxed{}$

$\qquad\quad m\angle 2 = \boxed{}$

On the Back!

5. What are $m\angle 1$ and $m\angle 2$?

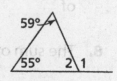

Use the list below to complete the sentences. Use each term once.

| exterior angle | interior angle | remote interior angles | supplementary |

1. A(n) _____ of a triangle is an angle
   formed by a side and an extension of an adjacent side.

2. Same-side interior angles are _____.

3. The nonadjacent interior angles corresponding to an exterior
   angle of a triangle are called _____.

4. A(n) _____ is an angle that is inside
   a shape.

For 5–8, use the diagram to complete each sentence.

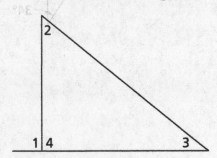

5. An exterior angle of the triangle is _____.

6. The remote interior angles of the triangle to the exterior angle 1
   are _____ and _____.

7. The sum of the measure of angles 2 and 3 is equal to the measure
   of _____.

8. The sum of the measure of angles 1 and 4 is _____.

Name _____

**Read the problem below. Then answer the questions to
identify the steps for solving the problem.**

In the diagram, $m\angle 1 = 65°$ and $m\angle 2 = 45°$. What are $m\angle 3$
and $m\angle 4$?

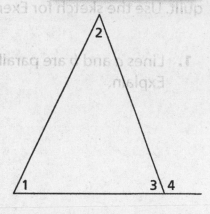

1. Label the diagram with the information that is given in
   the problem.

2. Circle the part or parts of the diagram that correspond to what you
   must find to solve the problem.

3. $\angle 4$ is an exterior angle of the triangle. What are the two remote
   interior angles of $\angle 4$? Explain.

4. Explain why $m\angle 1 + m\angle 2 = m\angle 4$.

5. Explain why $m\angle 3 + m\angle 4 = 180°$.

6. Do you have enough information to solve the problem? Explain.

Luann sketched this pattern as part of a design for a patchwork quilt. Use the sketch for Exercises 1–4.

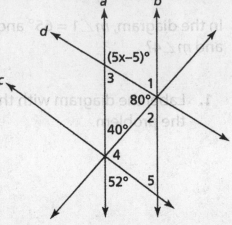

1. Lines *a* and *b* are parallel. What are $m\angle1$ and $m\angle2$? Explain.

2. What is $m\angle4$? Explain.

3. Are lines *c* and *d* parallel? Explain.

4. What is the value of *x*? Explain.

5. Luann's quilt will include patches shaped like equilateral triangles. What is the measure of an exterior angle of a patch? Explain.

Are the triangles similar? Explain.

The diagram shows that $\angle A \cong \angle F$.

Find $m\angle B$.

$$m\angle A + m\angle B + m\angle C = 180°$$
$$61° + m\angle B + 52° = 180°$$
$$113° + m\angle B = 180°$$
$$m\angle B = 67°$$

Therefore, $\angle B \cong \angle G$.

Because $\angle A \cong \angle F$ and $\angle B \cong \angle G$, $\triangle ABC \sim \triangle FGH$.

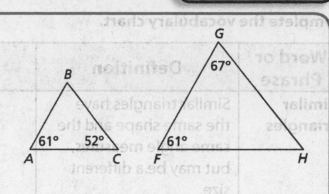

Are the triangles similar? Explain.

1. Explain why $\angle KLJ \cong \angle MLN$.

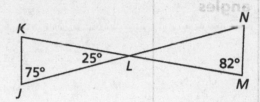

2. $\angle K$ and two other angles are the interior angles of a triangle. Complete the equation.

$$m\angle K + \boxed{} + \boxed{} = \boxed{}$$

3. Solve the equation in Exercise 2 to find $m\angle K$.

4. What equation can you use to find $m\angle N$? What is $m\angle N$?

5. Are the triangles similar? Explain.

On the Back!

6. Are the triangles similar? Explain.

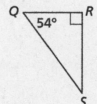

Complete the vocabulary chart.

Word or Phrase	Definition	Example
similar triangles	Similar triangles have the same shape and the same angle measures, but may be a different size.	
vertical angles		∠QXR and ∠ZXY are vertical angles.
transversal	A transversal is a line that crosses at least two other lines.	
AA (Angle-Angle) Similarity Criterion		△ABC ∼ △DEF

Name _____

Read the problem and connect it to the diagram.

Is △ABC~△DEC? Explain.

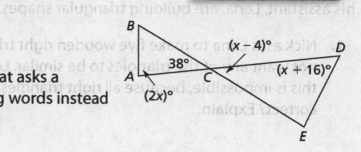

1. Underline the text in the problem that asks a
    question. Rewrite this question using words instead
    of mathematical symbols.

2. What can you check in order to determine whether △ABC~△DEC?

3. In the diagram, circle the expression $x - 4$. Then complete the
    equation below.

    $$x - 4 = \boxed{}$$

4. Explain why the angle that measures 38° has the same measure as the
    angle that measures $(x - 4)°$.

5. If you solve the equation in Exercise 3 to find the value of x, will
    you have shown that △ABC is similar to △EDC? Explain.

Name _____

Nick creates three-dimensional sculptures out of wood. Nick and his assistant, Lena, are building triangular shapes.

1. Nick asks Lena to make five wooden right triangles, and he does not want any of the triangles to be similar. Lena tells Nick that this is impossible, because all right triangles are similar. Is Lena correct? Explain.

2. Nick builds $\triangle PST$ and then adds $\overline{QR}$ so that $\overline{QR} \parallel \overline{ST}$. Is $\triangle PQR \sim \triangle PST$? Explain.

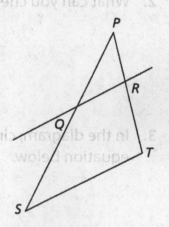

3. Lena tells Nick that she has created two isosceles triangles, and each triangle contains a 45° angle but they are not similar. Nick says that Lena's triangles must be similar. Is he correct? Explain.

4. Nick builds a triangle with a 71° angle and an angle that measures $(8x)°$. Lena builds a triangle in which the measures of two angles are 71° and $(7y)°$. Find a set of values for x and y which result in the two triangles being similar. Explain.

Name _____

Solve Problems Involving Surface Area and Volume

Dear Family,

Your child is learning to calculate the surface areas and volumes of cylinders, cones, and spheres. He or she will also solve related problems, such as finding volumes of composite figures and determining a missing dimension of a three-dimensional figure.

You can use the following activity to support your child's understanding of surface area.

Wrapping Cylinders

Materials: An object in the shape of a cylinder (such as an unopened can of food or an oatmeal box with its lid on), paper, scissors, ruler

Step 1 Ask your child to visually estimate the surface area of the cylinder in square inches or square centimeters.

Step 2 Have your child cut paper to exactly cover the cylinder, with no gaps and no overlaps. He or she will need to cut two circles and a rectangle.

Step 3 Have your child measure his or her circles and rectangle and use the measurements to calculate the surface area of the cylinder. Compare the result to his or her original estimate.

Observe Your Child

Focus on Mathematical Practices
Look for and make use of structure.

Help your child become proficient with this Mathematical Practice. Have your child compare the circumference of one of the circles to the width of the rectangle by rolling the circle along the width of the rectangle. Then ask him or her to explain the formula for surface area of a cylinder: S.A. = $2\pi r^2 + 2\pi rh$.

Resolver problemas de área total y volumen

> Estimada familia:
>
> Su hijo o hija está aprendiendo a calcular el área total y el volumen de cilindros, conos y esferas. También resolverá problemas relacionados, como hallar el volumen de figuras compuestas e identificar la dimensión que falta en una figura tridimensional.
>
> Puede usar esta actividad con su hijo o hija para reforzar su comprensión del área total.

Cilindros envueltos

Materiales: Un objeto con forma de cilindro (como una lata de alimentos sin abrir o un recipiente de avena con tapa), papel, tijeras, regla

Paso 1 Pida a su hijo o hija que estime visualmente el área total del cilindro en pulgadas cuadradas o en centímetros cuadrados.

Paso 2 Pídale que recorte un pedazo de papel que cubra exactamente todo el cilindro, sin dejar espacios descubiertos ni lugares donde se superponga el papel. Deberá recortar dos círculos y un rectángulo.

Paso 3 Pídale luego que mida los círculos y el rectángulo que recortó y que use las mediciones para calcular el área total del cilindro. Comparen los resultados con la estimación original.

Observe a su hijo o hija

Enfoque en las Prácticas matemáticas
Buscar y utilizar la estructura.

Ayude a su hijo o hija a adquirir competencia en esta Práctica matemática. Pídale que compare la circunferencia de uno de los círculos con el ancho del rectángulo haciendo rodar el círculo a lo largo del ancho del rectángulo. Luego, pídale que explique la fórmula del área total de un cilindro: $AT = 2\pi r^2 + 2\pi rh$.

To find how much paint she needs to paint a
cylinder, Simone first draws this net. What is the
surface area of the cylinder? Use 3.14 for π.

Find the area of each circle.

$A = \pi r^2$

$= \pi \cdot 2^2$

$= 4\pi$

≈ 12.56 in.^{2}

2 in.

9 in.

Find the area of the rectangle.
The rectangle's base is the
circumference of the circle, $C = 2\pi r$.

$A = bh$

$= 2\pi r \cdot h$

$= 2\pi(2) \cdot 9$

$= 36\pi$

≈ 113.04 in.^{2}

S.A. $\approx 12.56 + 12.56 + 113.04 = 138.16$ square inches

Sharlene wraps a cylindrical package that has a height of 15 inches and
a radius of 3 inches. What is the package's surface area? Use 3.14 for π.

1. What is the area of each circle?

$A = \pi r^2$

$= \pi \cdot \boxed{}^2$

$= \boxed{} \pi$

$\approx \boxed{}$ in.^{2}

2. Find the circumference of the circle and the area of the rectangle.

$C = 2\pi r$ $\qquad\qquad$ $A = bh$

$= 2\pi \cdot \boxed{}$ $\qquad\qquad$ $\approx \boxed{} \cdot \boxed{}$

$= \boxed{} \pi$ $\qquad\qquad$ $= \boxed{}$ in.^{2}

$\approx \boxed{}$ in.

3. What is the surface area of the cylinder?

S.A. $= \boxed{} + \boxed{} + \boxed{} = \boxed{}$ in.^{2}

On the Back!

4. What is the surface area of a cylindrical can with a radius of 3 centimeters
and a height of 11 centimeters? Use 3.14 for π.

Each box has a 3-D figure, a 2-D net, or a description of a three-dimensional figure. Write *cone, cylinder,* or *sphere* in each box.

1. A three-dimensional figure with two parallel circular bases that are the same size	**2.** 
3. A three-dimensional figure with one circular base and one vertex	**4.** 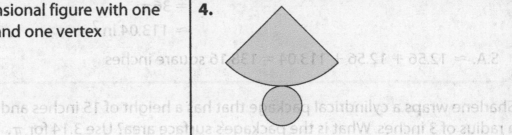
5. 	**6.** The set of all points in space that are the same distance from a center point
7. 	**8.** 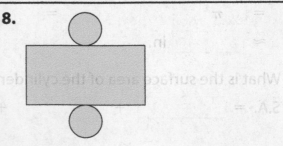

Name _____

A tent manufacturer makes a tent in the shape of a cone.
How much canvas is used to make this tent, including the floor?
Use 3.14 for π.

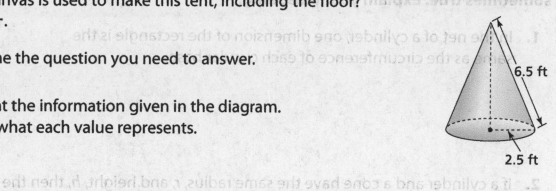

6.5 ft

2.5 ft

1. Underline the question you need to answer.

2. Highlight the information given in the diagram.
   Explain what each value represents.

3. What formula can you use to solve this problem? Explain.

4. Describe the correct answer to this problem, including the units.

5. Why does the problem tell you to use 3.14 for π? Explain how to
   use 3.14 to find the surface area.

Name _____

Tell whether each statement is always true, never true, or sometimes true. Explain your reasoning.

1. In the net of a cylinder, one dimension of the rectangle is the same as the circumference of each circular base.

2. If a cylinder and a cone have the same radius, r, and height, h, then the surface area of the cylinder is twice the surface area of the cone.

3. The surface area of a sphere is greater than or equal to 4π.

4. The area of the curved surface of a cone is greater than the area of its base.

5. If a cylinder and sphere have the same radius, r, then the surface area of the cylinder is greater than or equal to the surface area of the sphere.

What is the volume of this water heater? Use 3.14 for π.

Volume = area of base × height.
The base of a cylinder is a circle.

$V = Bh$
$= \pi r^2 \cdot h$
$= \pi(1)^2 \cdot 14$
$= 14\pi$
$\approx 21.98 \text{ ft}^3$

The volume of the water heater is about 21.98 cubic feet.

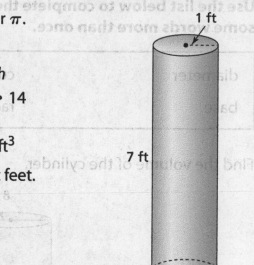

1 ft

7 ft

Jake wants to track the amount of water he drinks each day.
What is the volume of Jake's water bottle? Use 3.14 for π.

6 cm

1. What is the radius of the water bottle?

2. What is the area of the base?

$B = \pi r^2$

$= \pi(\boxed{})^2$

$= \boxed{}\,\pi$

$\approx \boxed{} \text{ cm}^2$

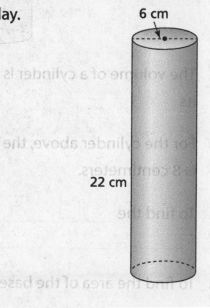

22 cm

3. What is the volume of Jake's water bottle?

$V = Bh$

$\approx \boxed{} \cdot \boxed{}$

$= \boxed{} \text{ cm}^3$

On the Back!

4. What is the volume of the cylindrical shipping tube?
Use 3.14 for π.

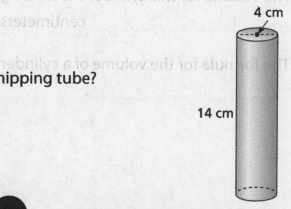

4 cm

14 cm

**Use the list below to complete the sentences. You may need to use
some words more than once.**

diameter	cubic	π
base	radius	$V = Bh$

Find the volume of the cylinder.

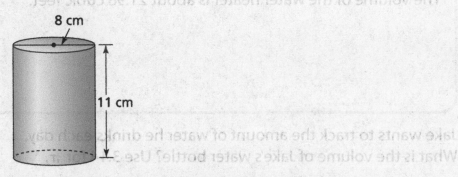

8 cm

11 cm

1. The volume of a cylinder is the product of its height and the area of
   its _____.

2. For the cylinder above, the _____ of the base
   is 8 centimeters.

3. To find the _____ of the base, divide the
   _____ by 2.

4. To find the area of the base, multiply the constant,
   _____, which is approximately 3.14, by the
   square of the _____.

5. The volume for this cylinder should be given in
   _____ centimeters, or cm³.

6. The formula for the volume of a cylinder is
   _____.

Name _____

Tiana compares the volumes of two different flour canisters.
Which canister holds more flour?

1. How is the amount of flour that each
    container holds related to the volume?

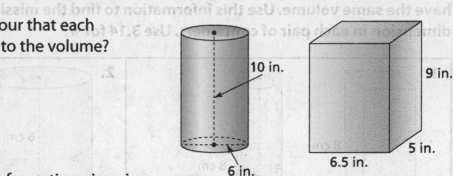

10 in.

9 in.

6 in.

6.5 in.

5 in.

2. Highlight the relevant information given in
    each diagram. Describe the dimensions of each container using
    the given information.

3. Will you need to find the volumes of both containers to solve this
    problem? Explain.

4. What is true about the volume of the container that holds
    more flour?

5. Do you have enough information to solve this problem? Explain.

**A pottery maker designs and sells salt and pepper shakers.
Although the containers in each pair have different shapes, both
have the same volume. Use this information to find the missing
dimension in each pair of containers. Use 3.14 for π.**

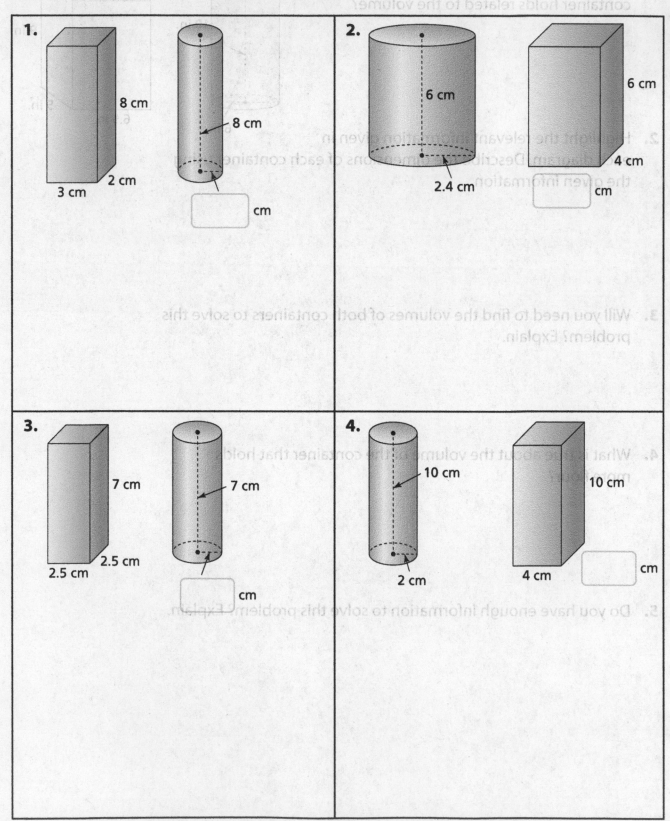

1.

8 cm

8 cm

2 cm

3 cm

☐ cm

2.

6 cm

6 cm

4 cm

2.4 cm

☐ cm

3.

7 cm

7 cm

2.5 cm

2.5 cm

☐ cm

4.

10 cm

10 cm

2 cm

4 cm

☐ cm

Marta is using several small colorful cones to decorate her house for a party. What is the volume of the cone at the right? Use 3.14 for π.

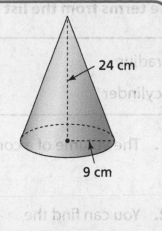
24 cm

9 cm

Volume $= \frac{1}{3} \times$ area of base $\times$ height. $V = \frac{1}{3}Bh$

The base of a cone is a circle. $V = \frac{1}{3}\pi r^2 h$

$\qquad\qquad\qquad\qquad V = \frac{1}{3} \cdot \pi(9)^2 \cdot 24$

$\qquad\qquad\qquad\qquad\quad = 648\pi$

$\qquad\qquad\qquad\qquad\quad \approx 2{,}034.72 \text{ cm}^3$

The volume of the cone is about 2,034.72 cubic centimeters.

A frozen-yogurt shop offers extra-large waffle cones. What is the volume of the waffle cone? Use 3.14 for π and round to the nearest hundredth.

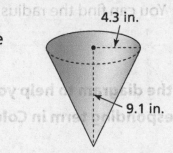
4.3 in.

9.1 in.

1. What are the radius, r, and height, h, of the waffle cone?

   $r =$ ⬚ inches $h =$ ⬚ inches

2. What is the area of the base?

   $B = \pi r^2$

   $\quad = \pi($ ⬚ $)^2$

   $\quad =$ ⬚ π

   $\quad \approx$ ⬚ in.^{2}

3. What is the volume of the waffle cone?

   $V = \frac{1}{3}Bh$

   $\quad = \frac{1}{3} \cdot$ ⬚ $\cdot$ ⬚

   $\quad \approx$ ⬚ in.^{3}

On the Back!

4. What is the volume of the cone? Use 3.14 for π.

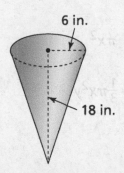
6 in.

18 in.

Use terms from the list below to complete the sentences.

radius	circumference
cylinder	

1. The volume of a cone is equal to one third of the volume of a
   _____ with the same radius and height.

2. You can find the _____ of the base of a cone if you
   know the cone's height and volume.

3. You can find the radius of a cone if you know the
   _____ of the base.

**Use the diagram to help you match each expression in Column A to the
corresponding term in Column B.**

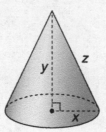

Column A

4. $2\pi x$

5. y

6. z

7. πx^2

8. $\frac{1}{3}\pi x^2 y$

Column B

slant height

area of base

volume of cone

circumference of base

height

Ed bought a cone full of pumpkin seeds at the county fair.
What is the volume of the cone? Write an exact answer in
terms of π.

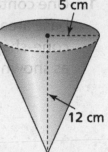

5 cm

12 cm

1. Underline the question in the problem.

2. Describe the correct answer to this problem, including the units.

3. Circle the dimensions in the diagram. What does each dimension
   represent?

4. How can you find the area of the base of the cone?

5. How can you use the area of the base to find the volume of
   the cone?

Emily has a collection of plastic containers shaped like cylinders and cones. Solve each problem about Emily's containers without using a calculator.

1. One container is a cylinder whose height is 9 inches and whose base area is 12 square inches. What is the volume of the largest cone-shaped container that can fit inside the cylindrical container as shown? Explain.

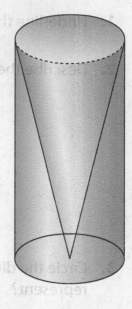

2. A cone-shaped container has a height of 5 inches and a base area of 6 square inches. What is the volume of the smallest cylindrical container that this cone can fit inside? Explain.

3. Emily places a cone-shaped container whose volume is 21 cubic inches upside down inside a cylindrical container as shown, creating a watertight seal. The containers have the same heights and base areas. Emily then pours water to fill the remaining space in the cylinder. What is the volume of water that Emily pours? Explain.

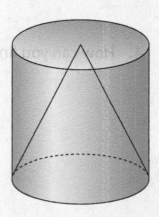

4. Emily has two identical cylinders and six identical cones. The combined volume of the cylinders is equal to the combined volume of the cones. The cylinders' diameters are $4\frac{1}{2}$ inches and the heights are 7 inches. What is the height of each cone?

What is the volume of the cylinder? Use 3.14 for π.

$V = \frac{4}{3}\pi r^3$ Formula for volume of a sphere

$= \frac{4}{3}\pi(6)^3$ The diameter of the ball is

$= 288\pi$ 12 centimeters, so the radius is
12 ÷ 2 = 6 centimeters.

≈ 904.32 cm^3

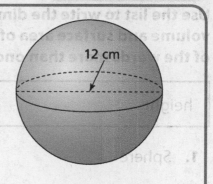

12 cm

The volume of the ball is about 904.32 cubic centimeters.

Marcus is using small stone spheres as garden decorations. What is
the volume of the stone sphere at the right? Use 3.14 for π.

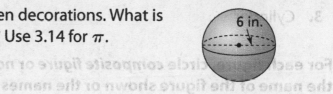

6 in.

1. What is the radius of the stone sphere?

2. What is the volume of the stone sphere?

$V = \frac{4}{3}\pi r^3$

$= \frac{4}{3}\pi(\boxed{})^3$

$= \frac{4}{3}\pi(\boxed{})$

$= \boxed{}\ \pi$

$\approx \boxed{}$ in.^{3}

3. Another stone sphere for the garden has a diameter of 10 inches.
   What is the volume of this stone? Use 3.14 for π, and round to the
   nearest hundredth.

On the Back!

4. According to the International Tennis Federation, the diameter of a
   standard tennis ball is 2.6 inches. What is the volume of a standard
   tennis ball? Use 3.14 for π, and round to the nearest hundredth.

**Use the list to write the dimensions that can be used to find the
volume and surface area of each figure. You will need to use some
of the words more than once.**

height	slant height	radius

1. Sphere _____

2. Cone _____

3. Cylinder _____

**For each figure, circle *composite figure* or *not a composite figure*. Then circle
the name of the figure shown or the names of the figures that make up the
composite figure.**

4.

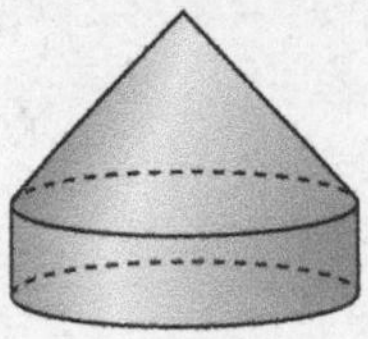

composite figure   not a composite figure

sphere   hemisphere

cone   cylinder

5.

composite figure   not a composite figure

sphere   hemisphere

cone   cylinder

6.

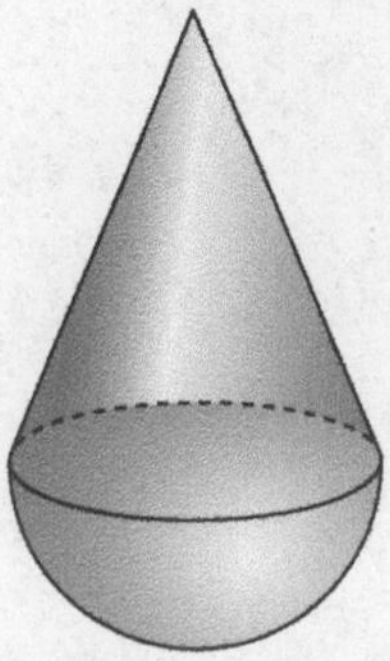

composite figure   not a composite figure

sphere   hemisphere

cone   cylinder

A human hamster ball is used for recreation.
What is the volume of the hamster ball?
Use 3.14 for π.

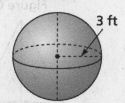

3 ft

1. Underline the question you need to answer.

2. Highlight the dimension in the diagram. What does the
   dimension represent?

3. Circle the calculation you should perform to find the volume of the
   human hamster ball.

   $V = \frac{4}{3}\pi(3)^2$ $\qquad\qquad$ $V = \frac{4}{3}\pi(6)^3$

   $V \approx \frac{3}{4}\left(\frac{22}{7}\right)(3)^3$ $\qquad\qquad$ $V \approx \frac{4}{3}(3.14)(3)^3$

4. Doing only mental calculations, determine if the volume of the
   human hamster ball is greater than or less than 27 cubic feet.

5. Write a formula you could use to make a quick estimate of the
   volume of any sphere.

A craft store sells clay in spheres with radius *r*. A sculptor
uses these spheres of clay to create composite figures.
Three composite figures that the sculptor makes are
shown in the diagrams.

1. How many spheres of clay does
the sculptor need to make two
copies of Figure A? Explain.

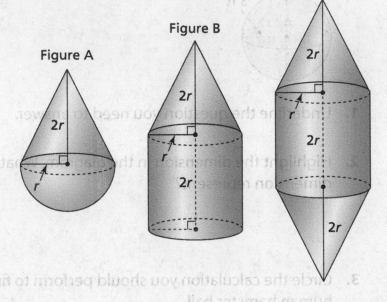

Figure A

Figure B

Figure C

2. How many spheres of clay does the sculptor need to make two
copies of Figure B? Explain.

3. How many copies of Figure C can the sculptor make from
15 spheres of clay? Explain.

Name _____

Self-Assessment Tool

I am on the road to understanding...

Mark an X on the road to show where you are.

 I don't understand.

 I understand a little.

 I think I understand.

 I really understand!

Road to Success

Explain the choice you made above.

Definition

Characteristics

Examples

Non-Examples

New Word	What It Means

Name _____

Examples:

Related Words:

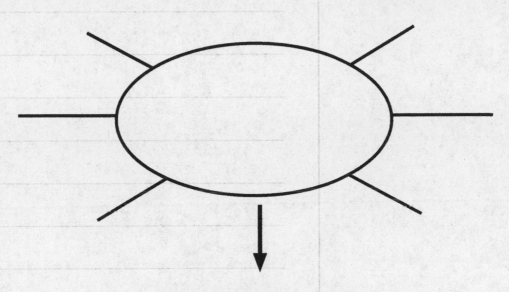

Tell About It:

_____

_____

_____

_____

_____

_____

_____

_____

_____

New Symbol	**What It Means:**
	_____
	_____
	_____
	_____
	_____
	_____

New Shape	**Name and Attributes:**
	_____
	_____
	_____
	_____
	_____
	_____
	_____

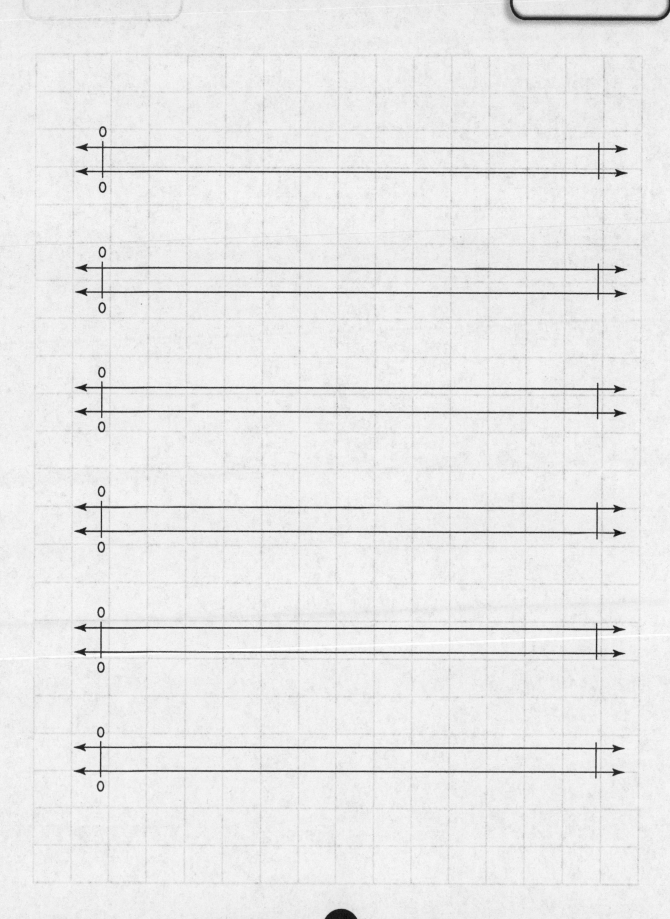

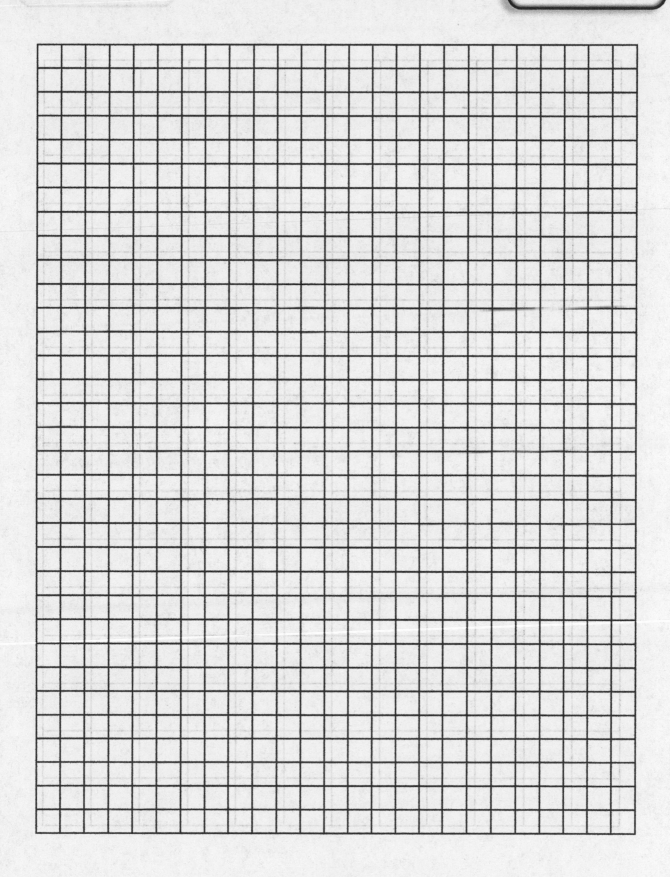

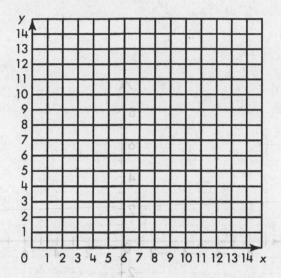

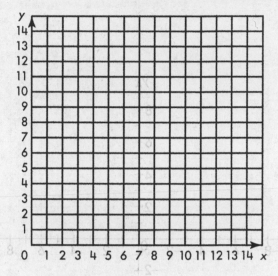

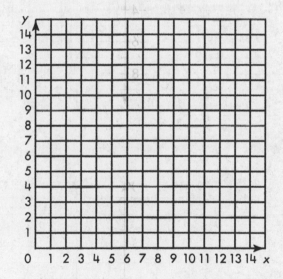

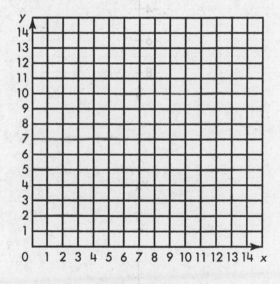

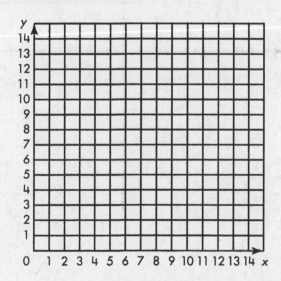

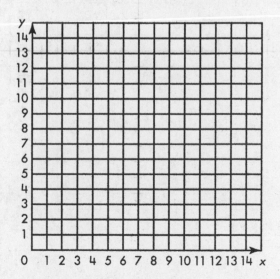

First Quadrant Coordinate Grids   13

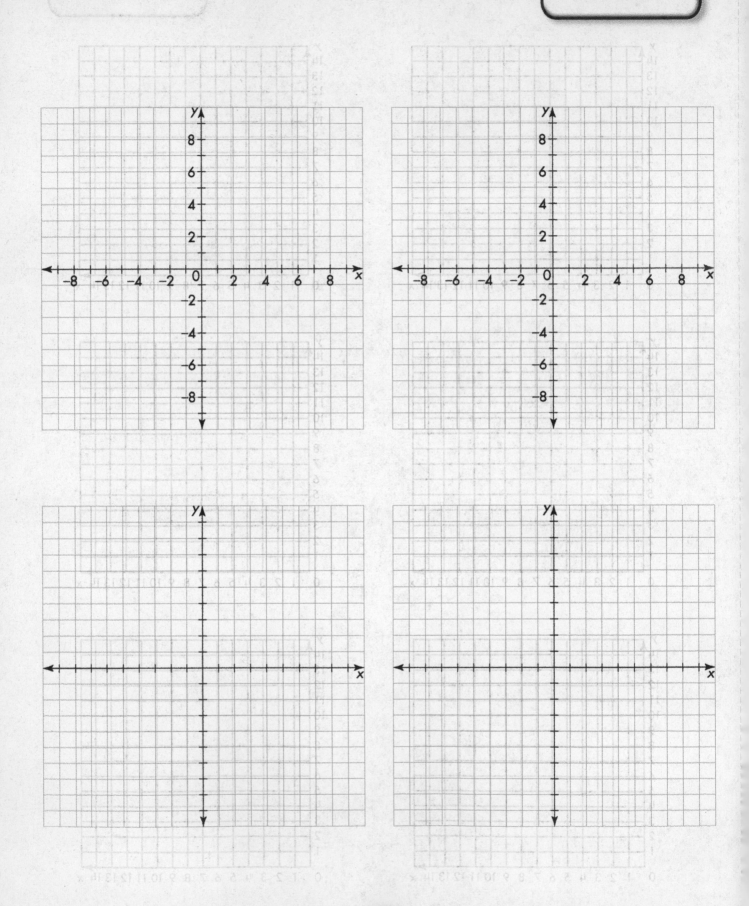

Name ______________________________

Teaching Tool
15

	0	
1	2	3
4	5	6
7	8	9

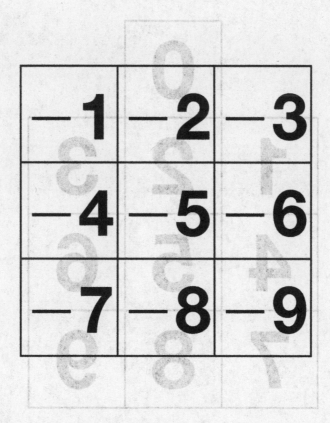

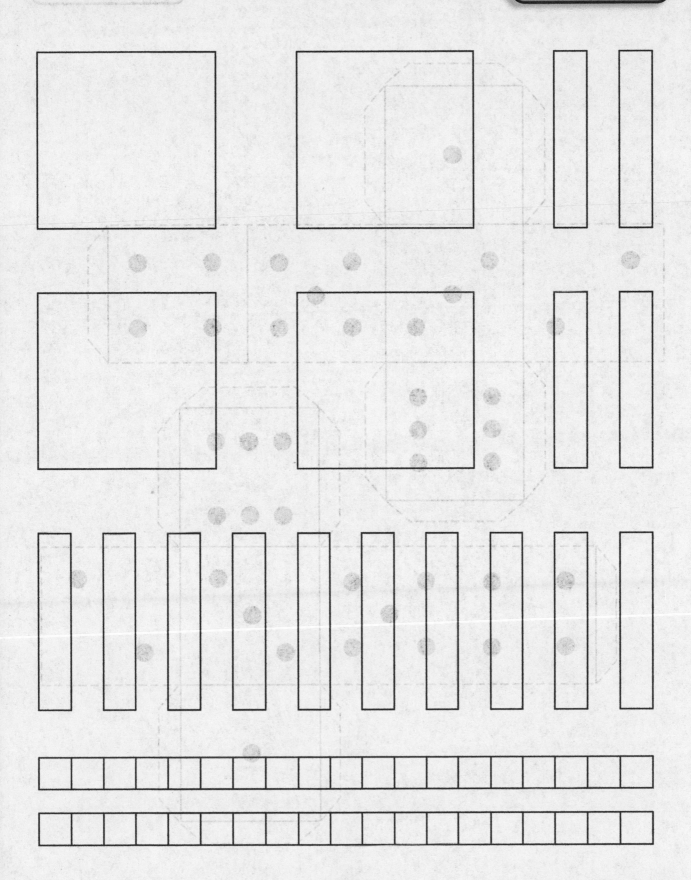

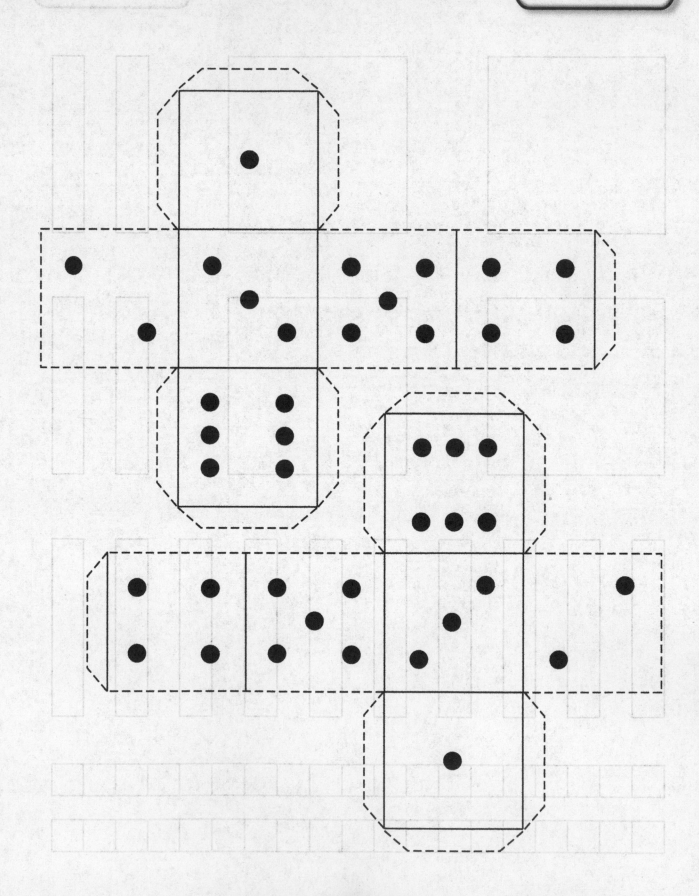

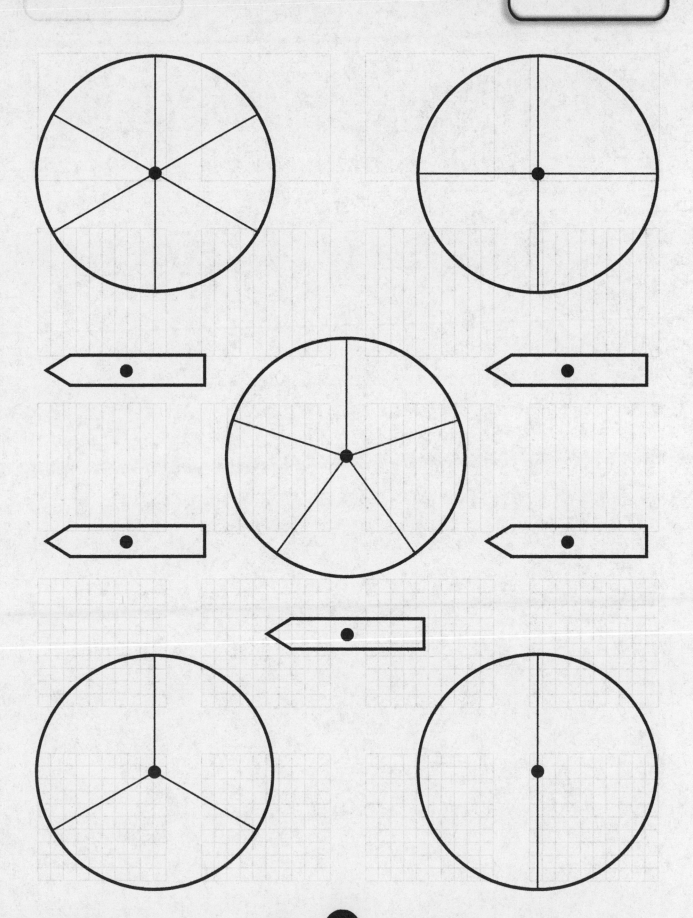

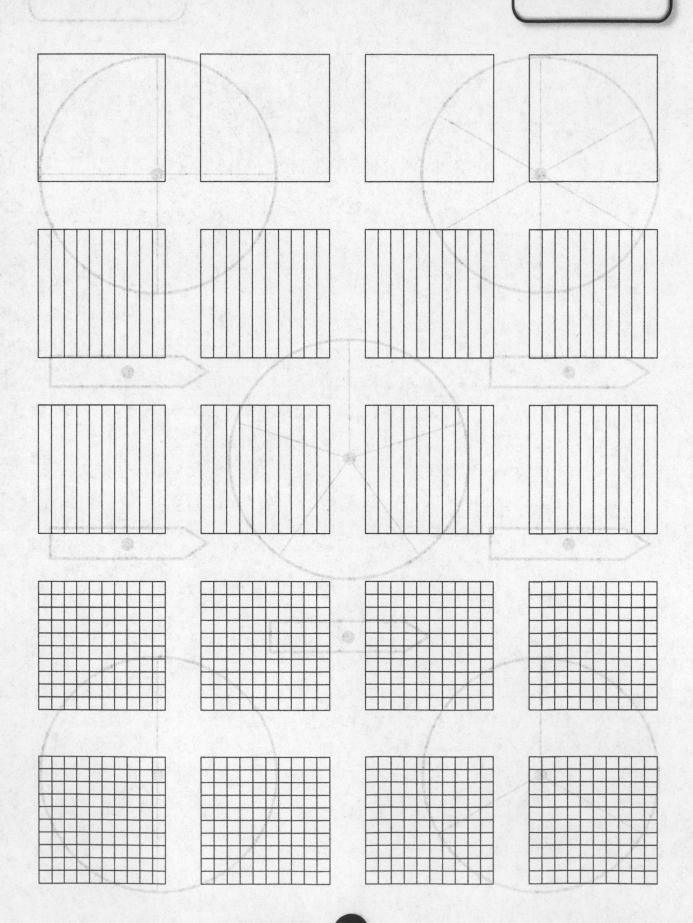

CENTIMETERS

0 1 2 3 4 5 6 7 8 9 10 11 12 13 14 15 16 17 18 19 20

CENTIMETERS

CENTIMETERS

CENTIMETERS

CENTIMETERS

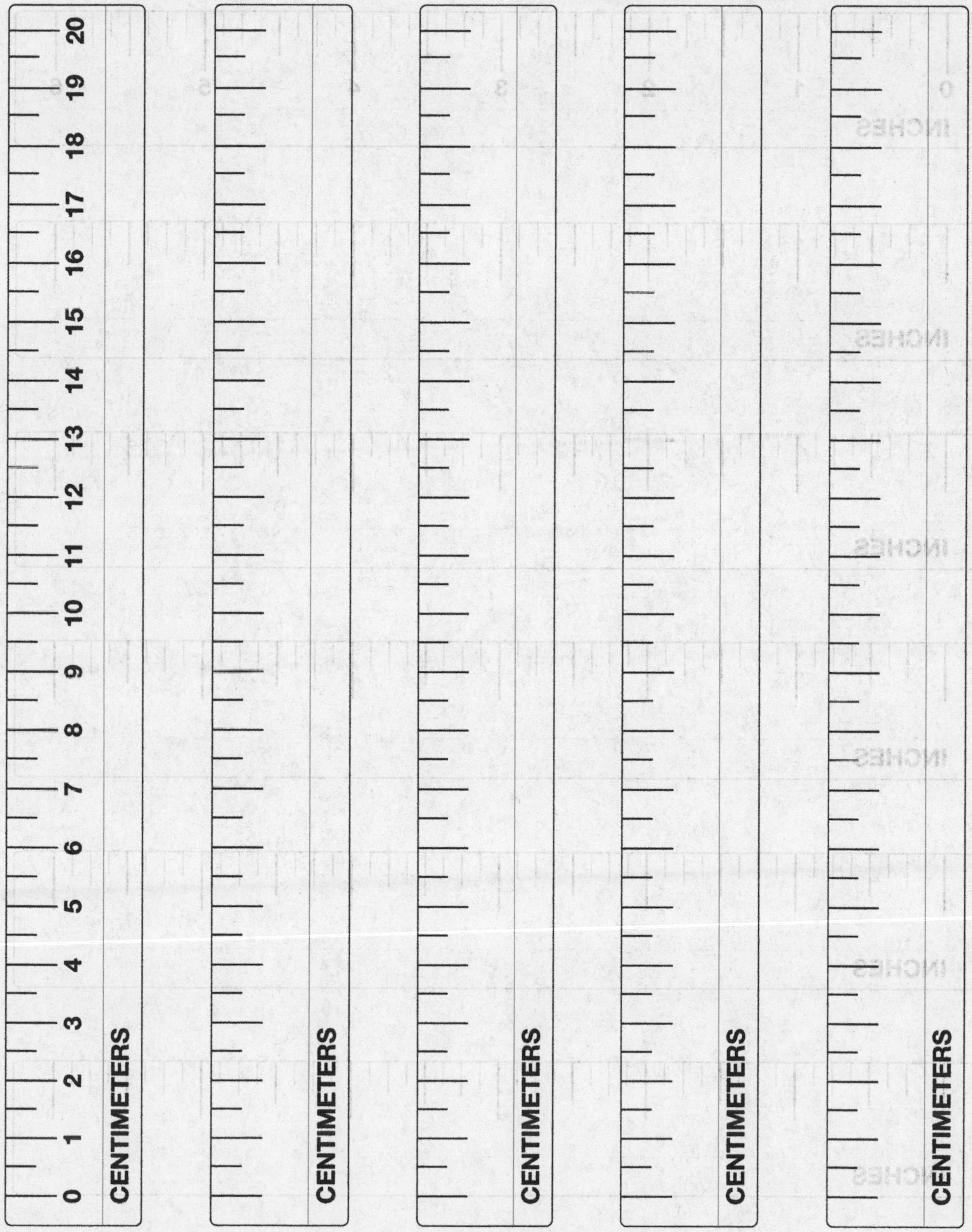

(To form a meter stick, cut out and tape five rulers together and complete labeling.)

INCHES

0   1   2   3   4   5   6

INCHES

INCHES

INCHES

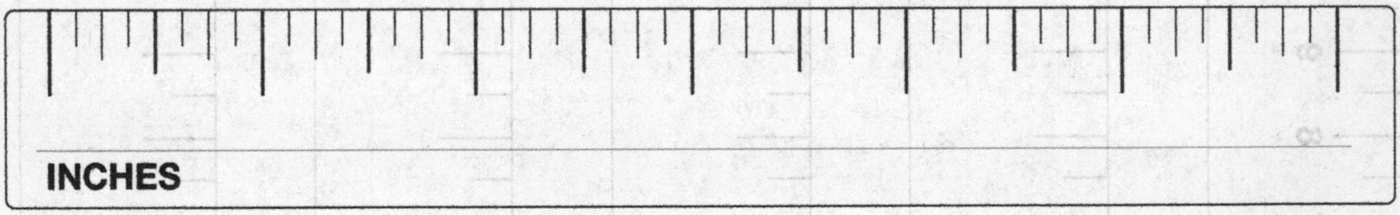

INCHES

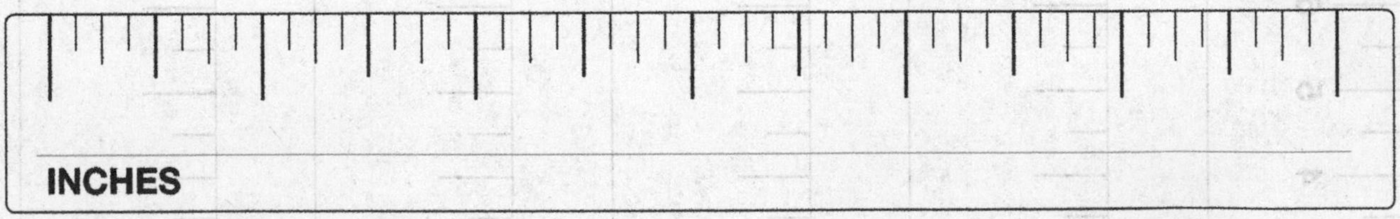

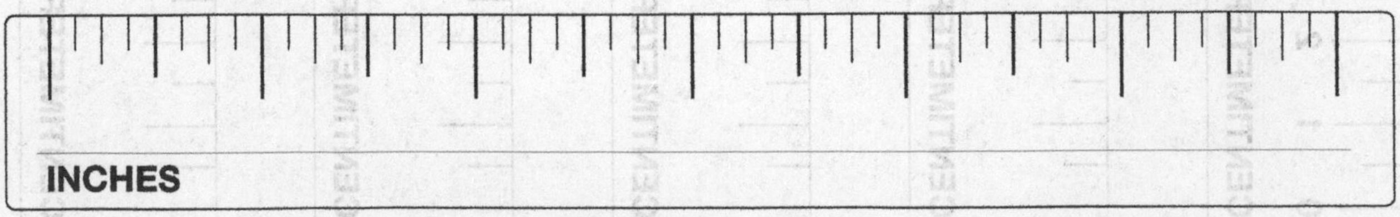

INCHES

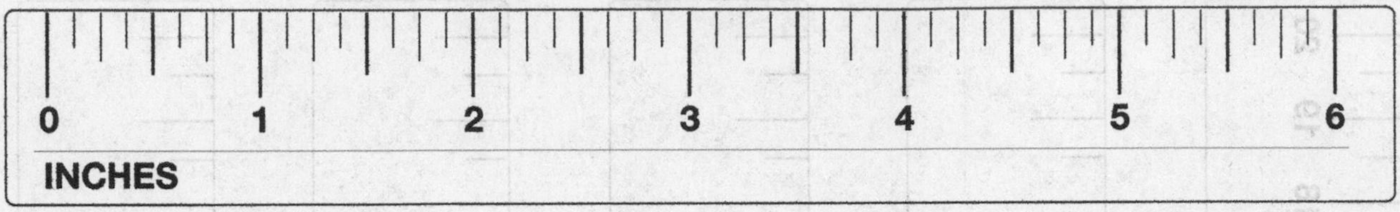

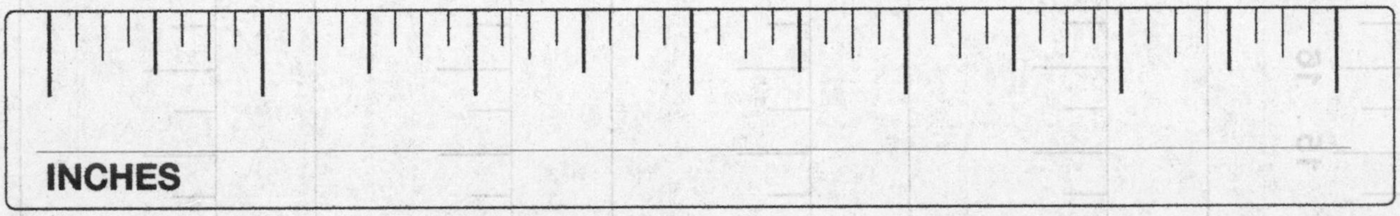

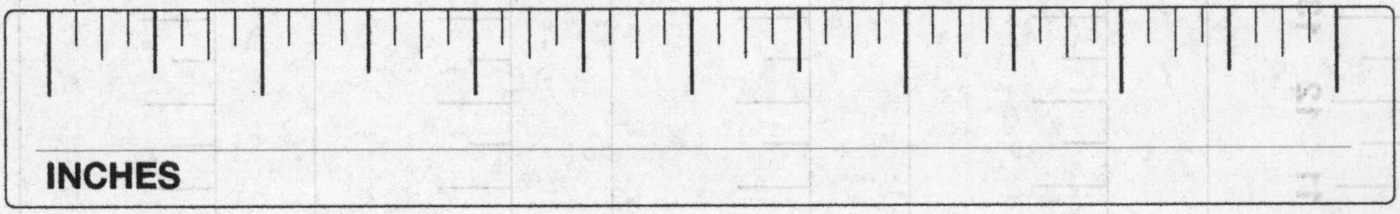

(To form a yardstick, cut out and tape six rulers together and complete labeling.)

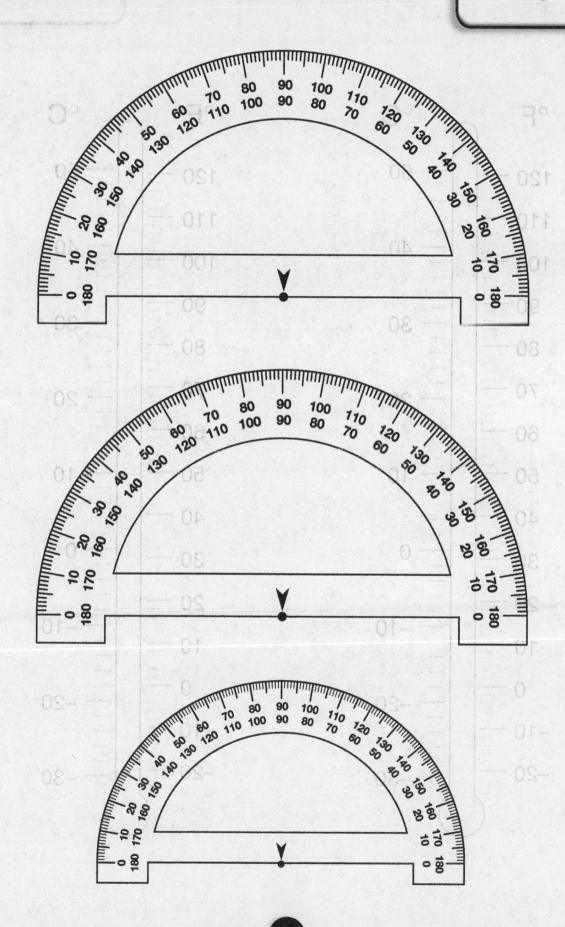

°F	°C	°F	°C
120	50	120	50
110	40	110	40
100		100	
90	30	90	30
80		80	
70	20	70	20
60	10	60	10
50		50	
40	0	40	0
30		30	
20	−10	20	−10
10		10	
0	−20	0	−20
−10		−10	
−20	−30	−20	−30

Name _____

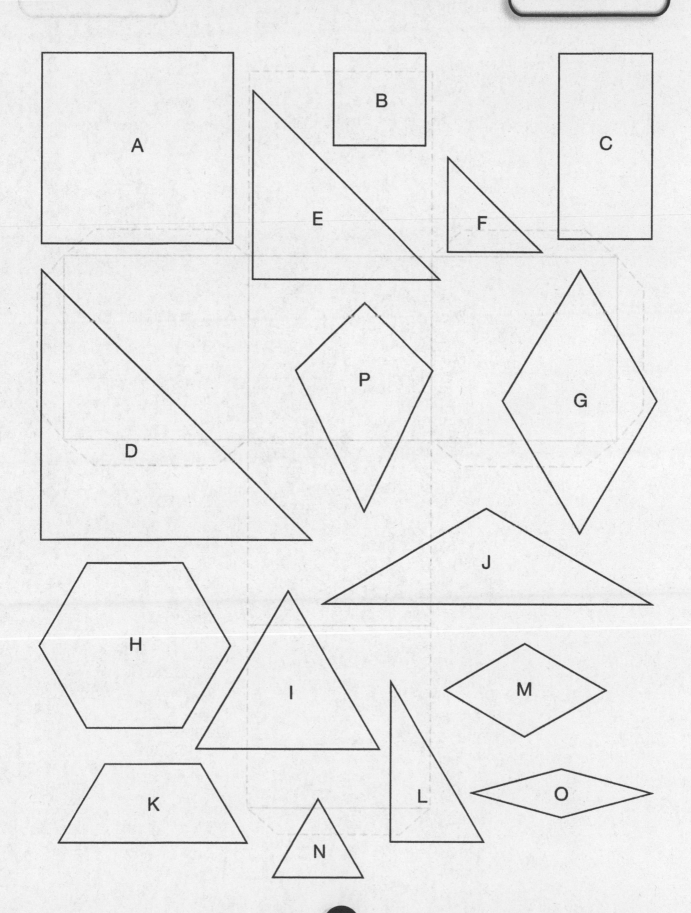

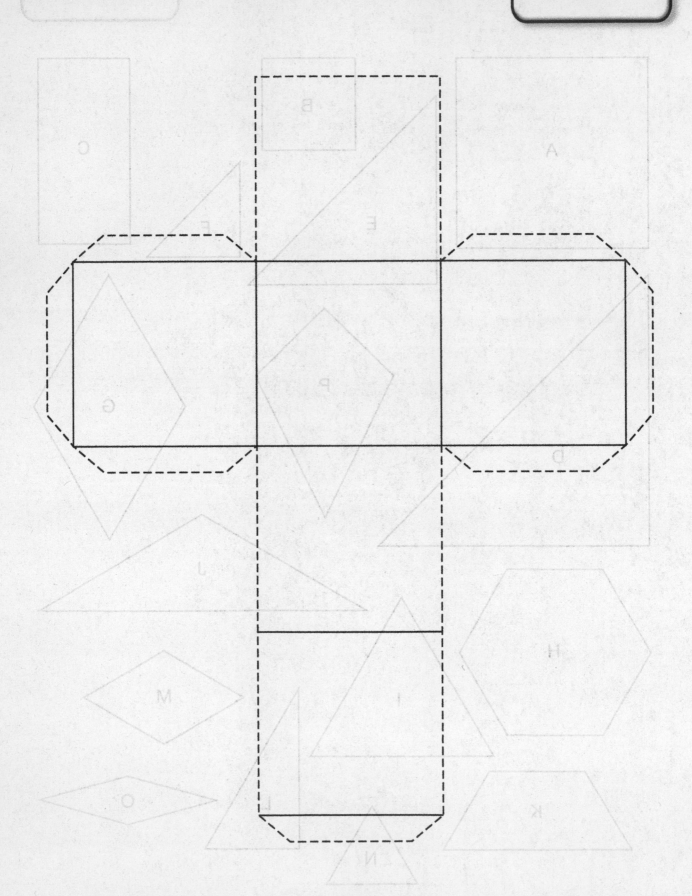

Name _____

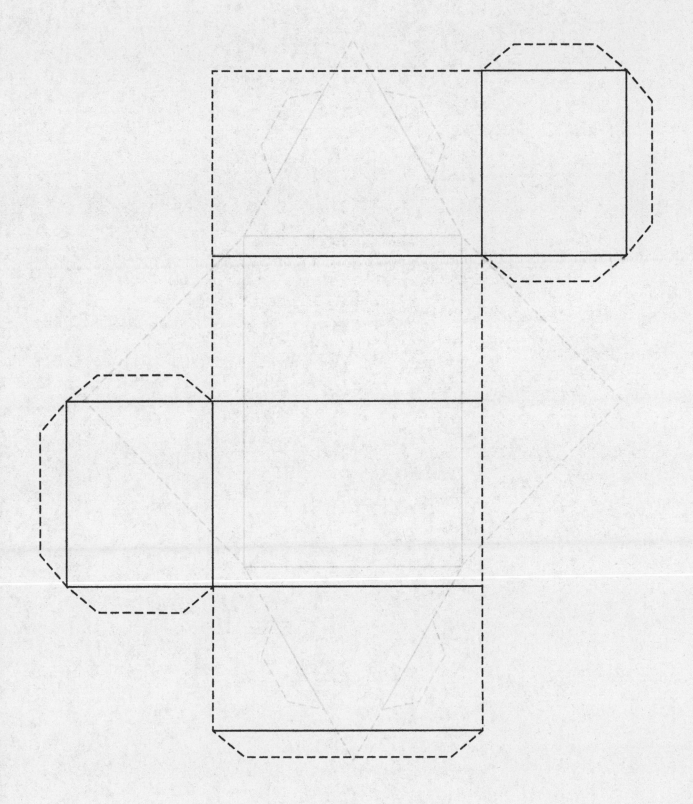

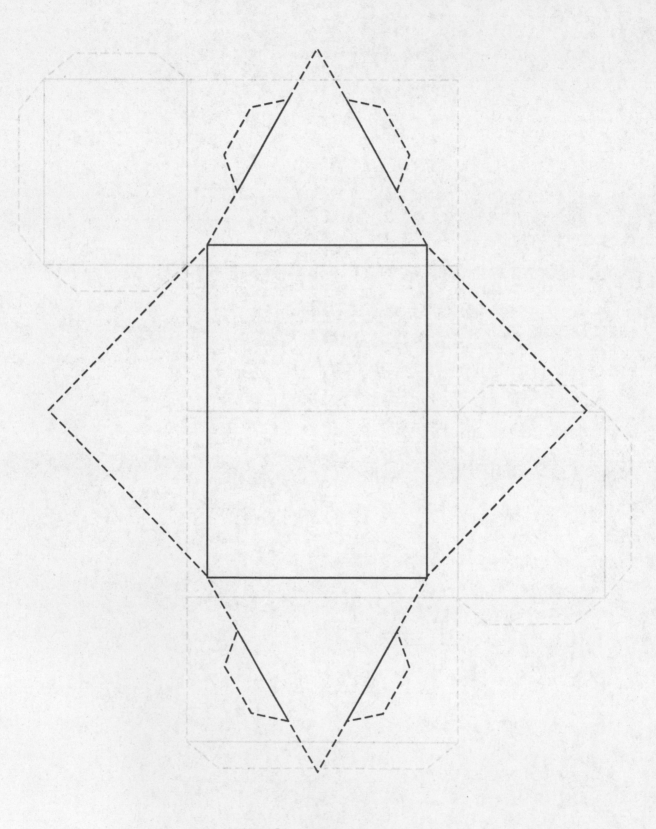

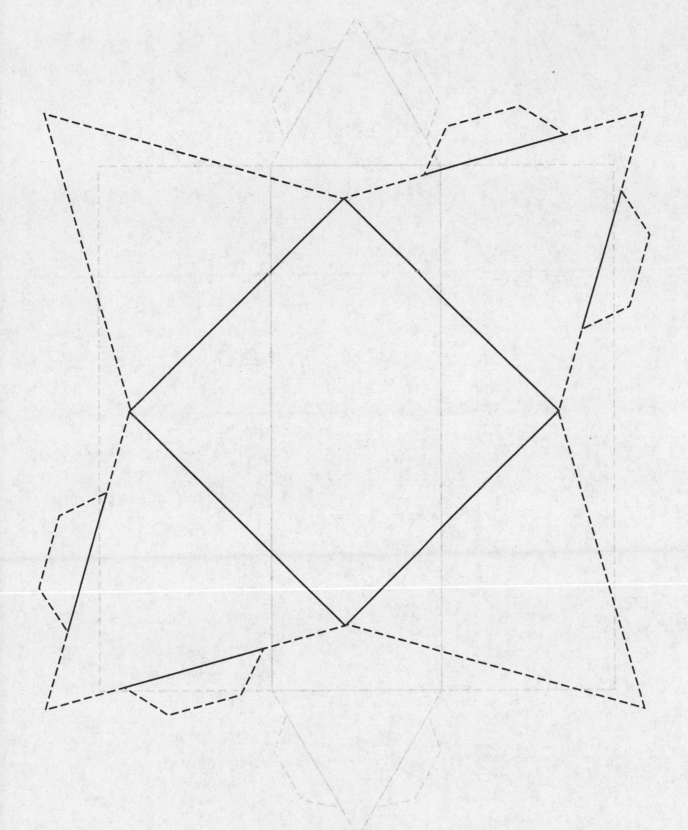

Net for Square Pyramid 29 7

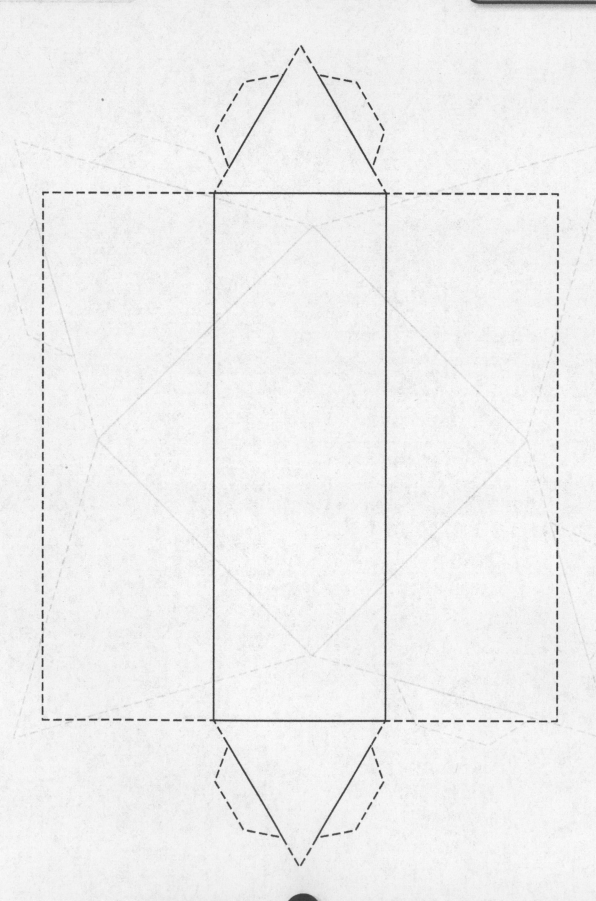

Net for Triangular Prism 30

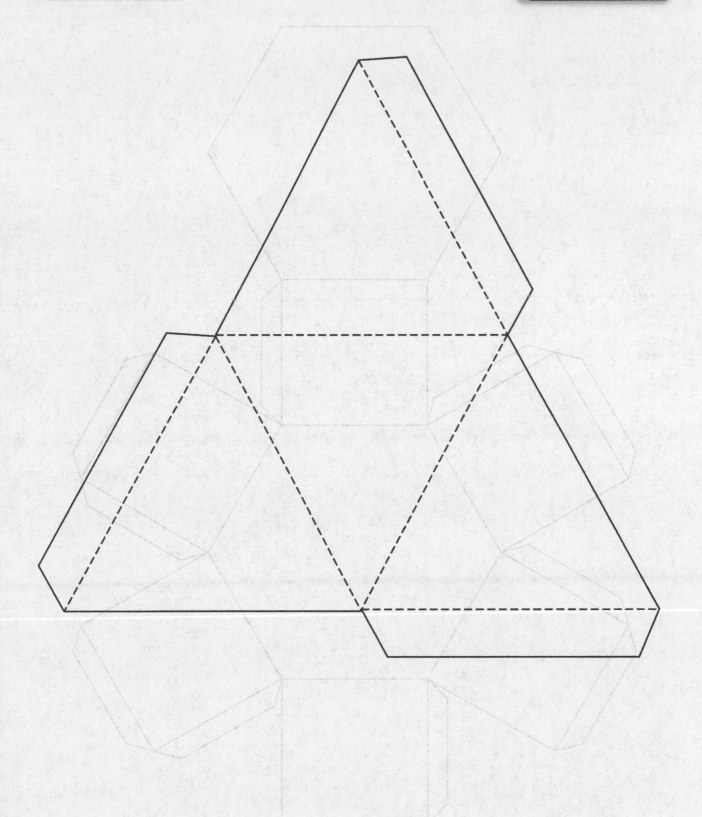

Net for Triangular Pyramid 31

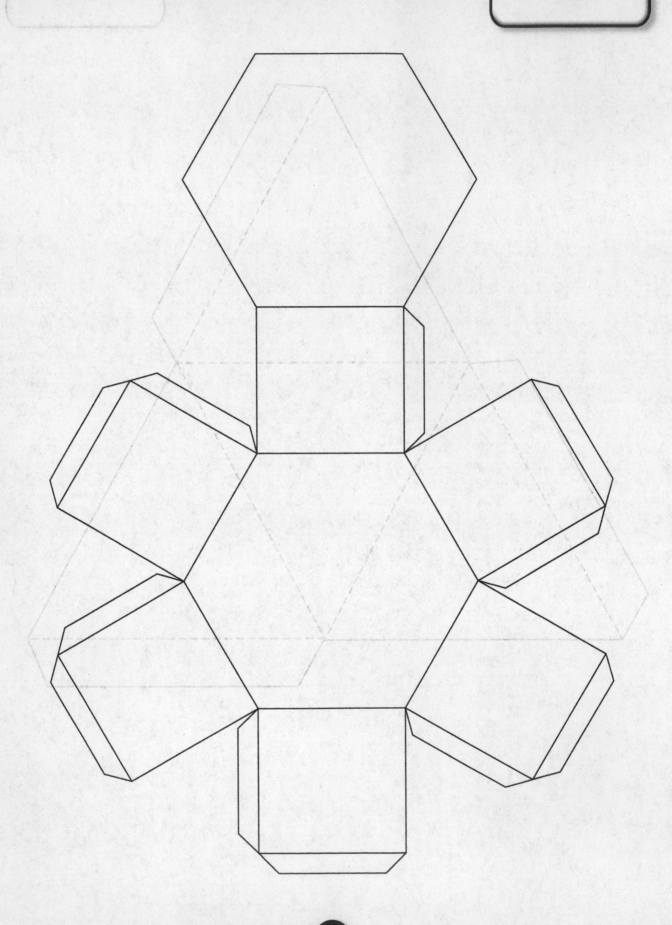

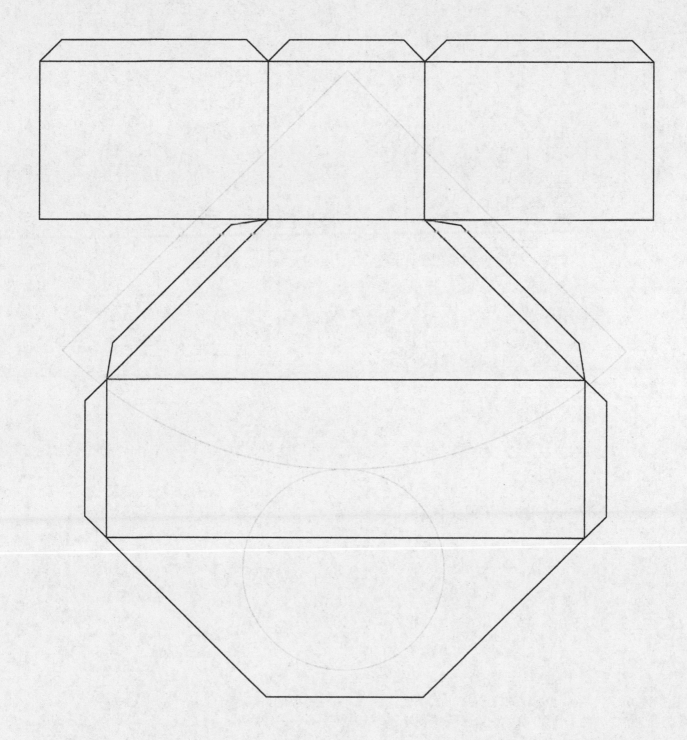

Net for Trapezoidal Prism 33

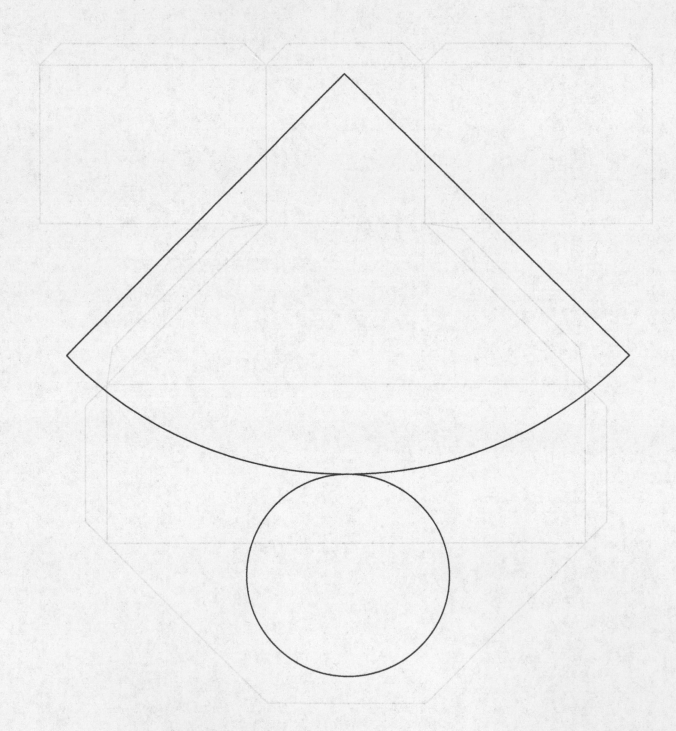

	Tallies	Frequency

	Tallies	Frequency

	Tallies	Frequency

	Tallies	Frequency

	Tallies	Frequency

	Tallies	Frequency

	Tallies	Frequency

	Tallies	Frequency